The Greatest Single Feature . . . A Sky-Line Drive

75 Years of a Mountaintop Motorway

Reed L. Engle, ASLA

Cultural Resource Specialist, Shenandoah National Park

Text by Reed L. Engle
Illustrations provided by Shenandoah National Park Archives or as noted on page 130
Editing by Joanne Amberson
Shenandoah National Park archival photography and photograph editing by John Amberson
Designed by Cindy Wilson Design
Project Coordination by Greta Miller

Printed in the United States of America by the Shenandoah National Park Association, a non-profit organization which supports the interpretive and educational activities in Shenandoah National Park. Profits from sales of publications, pamphlets, and maps are used to assist the park's interpretive program. If you would like to become a member of the Association or get further information and a list of publications available for purchase, contact:

Shenandoah National Park Association
3655 US Hwy 211 E.
Luray, VA 22835
540-999-3582
www.snpbooks.org

ISBN 0-931606-31-4

Printed in USA by Good Printers, Bridgewater, VA
Printed on Recycled Paper

To

John and Joanne Amberson

Who Have Given Over 20,000 Hours of Their Time
To Help Preserve and Interpret Shenandoah National Park.

Acknowledgments

A work of nonfiction is not created in a vacuum. Mountains of reference material must be found, copied, and assimilated. Researchers depend upon the kindness of strangers in this quest. The staff of the National Archives II, College Park, Maryland, was helpful and professional in their assistance. Philip J. Stenger (University of Virginia, Virginia State Climatology Office) provided invaluable data on the 1929/1930 drought. Ella Ross, SNP Archivist, offered assistance in finding important historical resources. John Amberson, SNP Archives volunteer, spent many, many hours finding suitable historic images and scanning and improving them so that they would be suitable for publication. This book would not have been possible without John's efforts.

Elizabeth Engle and Peter Dingman provided assistance in interpreting the legal meaning of the original park rights-of-way and deed transfers for a legalese-challenged author. Karen Michaud, SNP Chief of Interpretation and Education, and Sharon Henry, SNP Natural and Cultural Resources Division, reviewed portions of the text and provided insightful and heeded advice. Joanne Amberson, park volunteer in the Division of Interpretation and Education, again served as copy editor, correcting my consistent failure either to remember or to follow the NPS Style Manual and reminding me of the rules for commas and ellipses and, on occasion, calling me to task for bias.

Greta Miller, Executive Director, and the volunteer Board of Directors of the Shenandoah National Park Association (SNPA) supported and funded the publication of this book, the fourth in the park cultural history series produced over the past decade. Without the support and encouragement of SNPA, a balanced understanding of the significance of Shenandoah National Park's past would not have been possible.

My wife and partner Dolores Dyson Engle has again managed to coexist with me during the birthing process of this book. She has lived with the massive piles of document photocopies, accepted my daily detachment as I have worked on or thought through a concept, and improved my many drafts immeasurably.

Although many have helped review this book, mistakes are fully the responsibility of the author.

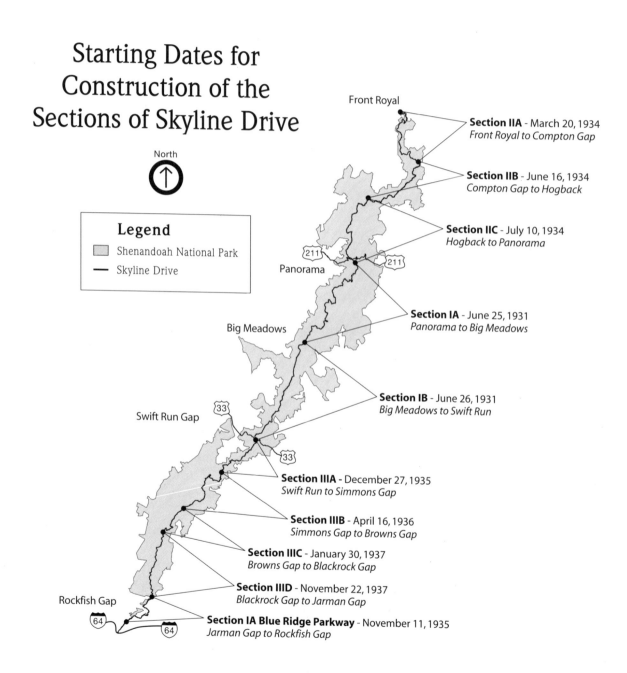

Starting Dates for Construction of the Sections of Skyline Drive

North

Legend
Shenandoah National Park
— Skyline Drive

Front Royal

Section IIA - March 20, 1934
Front Royal to Compton Gap

Section IIB - June 16, 1934
Compton Gap to Hogback

Section IIC - July 10, 1934
Hogback to Panorama

Panorama

Section IA - June 25, 1931
Panorama to Big Meadows

Big Meadows

Section IB - June 26, 1931
Big Meadows to Swift Run

Swift Run Gap

Section IIIA - December 27, 1935
Swift Run to Simmons Gap

Section IIIB - April 16, 1936
Simmons Gap to Browns Gap

Section IIIC - January 30, 1937
Browns Gap to Blackrock Gap

Section IIID - November 22, 1937
Blackrock Gap to Jarman Gap

Rockfish Gap

Section IA Blue Ridge Parkway - November 11, 1935
Jarman Gap to Rockfish Gap

Table of Contents

List of Illustrations

List of Tables

List of Photographs

"He who chooses the beginning of a road chooses the place it leads to.

It is the means that determine the end."

Harry Emerson Fosdick

"Long is the road from conception to completion."

Molière

Foreward

When I was a child, Sunday afternoons were for driving. The lean years of World War II were over. Young families with new, or almost new, automobiles took advantage of the "day of rest" (there were Blue Laws, and most stores were closed on Sundays) to take a drive in the country. And if you lived in the country, your parents called on friends whom they might not have seen since the previous Sunday.

Sunday drives were adventures, with the ever-present possibility of danger. In summer, families traveling two-lane roads with names a century old often ended up in traffic jams because radiators boiled over regularly. Car owners carried patching kits because tires had tubes and often went flat. Automobile air conditioning was unknown, and most vehicles had no radios. Travelers talked and played games.

Family vacations now were dependent on the automobile, and the trip itself became as important as the destination. Sightseeing along the way became a major part of the vacation. In the first half of the 20th century, roadside attractions sprang up like mushrooms after rain: Wall Drugstore (South Dakota, 1931); Roadside America (Pennsylvania, 1941); South of the Border (South Carolina, 1950); and countless roadside attractions offering motorists everything from a chance to view the "world's largest ball of twine" (Kansas, 1953) to the awe-inspiring "World's Largest Ball of Barbed Wire" (Minnesota, 1950). Increased automobile travel generated "tourist courts" of tiny individual cabins that soon grew into more organized "motor hotels" (motels), but which still retained unique, often quirky, architectural characters—witness the national chain of concrete wigwams. The generation that came of age in the

Great Depression listened to Dinah Shore and took their children to "See the USA in [Their] Chevrolet."

It was a time of simple pleasures. No little hands held electronic games. No iPods distracted conversation. No laptop computers. No Internet. Television was still over the horizon. Movies at a theater, radio at home, and newspapers were the media.

The Skyline Drive was designed for travelers in this pre-technological America. It was planned with care for leisurely drives and picnics in the cool mountain air. It was to be both the access to a national park and a major part of the park experience. It was to be both the "getting there" and a part of the "there."

The creation of the Skyline Drive was plagued by the simple fact that Shenandoah National Park

by the depression relief Public Works Administration, this first major National Park Service park roadway in the East became a testing ground for new architectural and landscape design standards.

The Skyline Drive is testimony to the values of a less pressured society. Politics, perseverance, and the privation of the Great Depression created it. Its completion was the result of the efforts of wealthy businessmen, legislators, displaced Blue Ridge Mountain residents, and the unemployed young men enrolled by the Civilian Conservation Corps.

It still stands up to the purpose set forth by the Southern Appalachian National Park Committee in its report to the Secretary of the Interior:

> It will surprise the American people to learn that a national park site with fine scenic and recreational qualities can be found within a 3-hour ride of our National Capital and within a day's ride of 40,000,000 of our inhabitants . . . . The greatest single feature, however, is a possible sky-line drive along the mountain top, following a continuous ridge and looking down westerly on the Shenandoah Valley . . . and also commanding a view of the Piedmont Plain stretching easterly to the Washington Monument . . . . Few scenic drives in the world could surpass it. [1]

Reed L. Engle, ASLA

PHOTOGRAPH 1: Paul Bunyan & Babe the Blue Ox

In a time of increased automobile ownership and greater leisure time, Americans toured the country for both Sunday drives and vacations. Roadside attractions such as this gigantic Paul Bunyan and Babe the Blue Ox (Bemidji, Minnesota, 1937) competed for the tourists.

did not exist when most of the road was being designed and built. It was a park road constructed without a park. The limitations imposed on the initial road design by the narrow right-of-way would have to be corrected once the park was established.

Due to the efforts of landscape architects and engineers hired by Franklin Delano Roosevelt's Civilian Conservation Corps and funding provided

" . . . as soon as the roads gits in good order Will come over. I expect it will be the last of next Month or the first of April . . . and would be happy to see you and family When ever convenient."

Randolph Jefferson to his brother Thomas Jefferson,
February 24, 1813 [2]

Part One:

Roads and Parks Before the Skyline Drive

Travel in Early America

American cities first grew along the seaports of the East Coast because those were the locations where the immigrant ships by happenstance and calm waters had docked. In the colonial period most commerce moved by water, not by land. The great plantations of the South had private docks and landings from which to ship their indigo, rice, cotton, and tobacco and to which to import slaves and manufactured goods. New England seaports grew wealthy on the export of dried cod, whale oil, and furs and brought back wine, rum, spices, porcelain, textiles, and, of course, tea. The Mid-Atlantic States traded iron, lumber, grains, agricultural products, and livestock not only with England, but also with their neighboring colonial ports north and south. All of this commerce moved by small boats, barges, and sailing ships.

For the first several generations of European immigration extensive settlement and commerce were limited to those areas easily accessible to navigable water, that is, those east of or below the "fall line" formed by the junction of the Piedmont with the coastal plain. But as most eastern rivers and streams run west-to-east from the mountains, most inter-colonial travel was still dependent on the sea. By the mid-18th century some companies had formed to build small canals above the fall line, incorporating locks to allow mule-drawn barges to transport products to navigable waters in the Piedmont, but it would not be until well into the 19th century that major canal systems were flourishing.

Today we tend to visualize colonists journeying from place to place in horse-drawn carriages and stagecoaches. Such was rarely the case. People rode horses, they walked, or they did not travel at all. A survey taken in 1761 in Pennsylvania—then possibly the most advanced colony in terms of transportation—indicated that only eighteen families owned carriages. In 1755 General Braddock attempted to organize a baggage train for an expedition against Forts Duquesne and Niagara; even with the able assistance of Benjamin Franklin, the newly appointed Postmaster General, Braddock was able to hire only 155 Conestoga wagons from throughout Virginia, Maryland, and Pennsylvania. [3]

A survey conducted in 1789 by the first Postmaster General of the United States under the Constitution, Samuel Osgood of Massachusetts, found that there were only 2,000 miles of acceptable post roads (i.e., roads used for the delivery of mail) in the country.

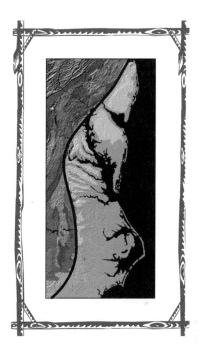

ILLUSTRATION 1: Map of Fall Line

Prior to 1792 American roads were built and maintained by local governments, in many cases following former bison trails or Indian paths. Road construction and maintenance was undertaken by mandatory road labor, for most municipalities were legally not allowed to levy road taxes. Males were required to provide several days of labor on local roads yearly or to pay a daily fee to avoid labor, or were assessed with a fine. Since most rural colonists were engaged in agricultural activities, roadwork sessions had to be scheduled around the agricultural calendar, typically occurring in late autumn or winter when good roadwork was impossible. America's westward expansion could not depend on transportation of goods by barge and boat; good roads were needed.

In 1806 Congress passed a bill to construct the nation's first federally funded highway, the Cumberland or National Road, to run from Cumberland, Maryland, to Wheeling, West Virginia, and on to the Ohio River. It was intended to open up the West to settlement, but was constitutionally justified as providing for military defense. But by 1830 the National Road was privatized and became a commercial toll road, following the trend of all transportation improvements in that era and one that had long before been introduced in England.

Great Britain, far in advance of her colonies, chartered its first private turnpike company to build a road in 1663, and by the American Revolution toll roads in England were common. The first private turnpike in America was chartered in Pennsylvania in 1792. It was to span 62 miles from Philadelphia to Lancaster, Pennsylvania, and serve as the primary route for transporting agricultural products from the "breadbasket of America." The road was completed by 1794 at a cost of $465,000 ($7,500/mile). The concept quickly gained national attention and by 1800 69 companies had received state charters to build private toll roads, primarily in the

northeastern states. By 1810 that figure had risen to 398. Private turnpike construction skyrocketed, but by 1840 the commercial frenzy had abated due to competition from more efficient canals and railroads.

The first American passenger train started service in Charleston, South Carolina, on Christmas Day 1830; its steam engine exploded in 1832. Trains realized speeds of 20 miles an hour and were not likely to become slowed by quagmires as road travelers were. By 1869 railroads would span the nation. Canals were flourishing—the 363-mile Erie Canal opened in 1825, incorporating 83 locks, and opening New York State's interior to commerce. Many canals and railroads, if not most, were state subsidized in some manner. Those

turnpikes being built were to serve as secondary routes feeding the railroads and canals.

Turnpikes, however, were expensive—many state charters required gravel and crushed stone construction that cost between $4,805-$13,455/mile. Additionally, many charters required that tolls be waived for those going to or from churches, funerals, polling places, town meetings, and/or to those living in a town within a mile of the turnpike or through which it passed. Most charters did not allow sufficient profit to attract investors. Investors found better returns for the money with the railroads. As a result, by 1845 more miles of toll roads were being abandoned than constructed.

TABLE 1: PRIVATE TURNPIKE INCORPORATIONS [4]

	1792-1810	1811-1830	1831-1845	TOTAL
NH	49	6	4	59
VT	28	22	7	57
MA	89	24	2	115
RI	16	21	4	41
CT	60	40	13	113
NY	139	208	110	457
PA	44	160	138	342
NJ	22	25	3	50
MD	12	45	21	78
VA	6	15	25	46
TOTAL	465	566	327	1,358

From 1847-1853 private road charters saw a rapid resurgence due to an inexpensive new road-building technique first used in Russia and introduced to America by Canada. "Plank" roads became popular, and 1,300 newly charted companies built over 10,000 miles in a six-year period, often upon the routes of former turnpikes. [5] Plank roads were simply two parallel rows of heavy timber "sleepers," 5'-6' apart, surfaced with 3"-4" thick, unsecured planks. Ditches were cut on either side of the road for drainage. As should have been, but apparently was not, expected, the wooden roads had a short life—often only 4-5 years, and were soon abandoned or reverted to dirt and/or gravel cart ways. With the exception of the American West, the private turnpike boom was over, and American roads in rural areas were quagmires in the spring and fall, dust bowls in the summer, and impassable in winter.

America was full into the age of steam and "America Moves By Rail" became more than a slogan. It was the reality from 1850 to 1920.

The Railroads and the National Parks

The National Park System owes its birth, in part, to Jay Cooke, the owner of the greatest private banking house in America in 1861. His firm raised almost $3,000,000,000 to support the Union cause in the Civil War and, in the process, he became one of the greatest barons of the age. In 1869 Cooke took over the finances of the faltering Northern Pacific Railroad. The company was chartered by Congress to build a transcontinental line from Duluth, Minnesota, to Seattle, Washington, and, in lieu of government financial assistance, was given a 39,000,000-acre grant of public lands in the west. Although new towns and industry were planned, little happened, and before Cooke became involved the charter appeared ready to be revoked. Cooke embarked on a campaign that resulted in the sale of $100,000,000 in Northern Pacific bonds and that led to the failure of his Jay Cooke & Company in 1873.

Cooke sent out an expedition in 1870 to survey the area near the railroad lands. On October 14, 1870, the *New York Times*, in what was probably a well-executed public relations effort, published a glowing account of the natural marvels seen by the members of the "Yellowstone Expedition."

Cooke wrote the following year:

> Judge Kelley [Senator William D. Kelley of Philadelphia] has made a suggestion which strikes me as being an excellent one, viz.: Let Congress pass a bill reserving the Great Geyser Basin [in Yellowstone] as a public park Forever—just as it has reserved that far inferior wonder the Yosemite Valley and big trees. [6]

It was evident to Cooke and other railroad magnates that setting aside the unique Yellowstone resources would eventually yield profits. Congress passed the Yellowstone Park Act on March 1, 1872. Eleven years later the Northern Pacific Railroad completed the Yellowstone Park Branch line from Livingston, Montana, to the park's northern entrance at Gardiner, eliminating a 100-mile stagecoach drive from the nearest rail depot. In the same year the railroad-financed Mammoth Hot Springs Hotel was completed, soon to be followed by the railroad-backed Lake Hotel and Old Faithful Inn.

The Northern Pacific Railroad retained a monopoly on rail access to Yellowstone until 1907, when the Union Pacific Railroad built a spur line to Yellowstone's western boundary and the terminus became the town of West Yellowstone. In time three other railroads developed lines to the neighboring towns of Cody and Lander, Wyoming, and Gallatin Gateway (Bozeman), Montana, where stagecoaches waited to speed wealthy visitors to the park. [7]

The patterns established by the railroads at Yellowstone were the standards for almost all of the early national parks (See TABLE 2). Yet although construction of rail lines made the parks more accessible to more people, particularly those not willing to ride for many, many days in crude stagecoaches just to get to the park entrance, park travel still remained the pursuit of the wealthy and those with much leisure time.

Yellowstone and the California national parks and national monuments were managed by the United States Army; the remaining were run by civilian superintendents or had no management at all.

TABLE 2: RAILROADS AND THE NATIONAL PARK SERVICE

Park/Monument Name	Date Est.	Railroad Involvement In Park
Yellowstone National Park	**1872**	Northern Pacific completed branch rail line to Gardiner in 1883 and completed the Mammoth Hot Springs Hotel in the park the same year, shortly to be followed by the Lake Hotel and Old Faithful Inn. Union Pacific Railroad reached West Yellowstone in 1907.
Mackinac Island National Park (Given back to State of Michigan in 1895)	**1875**	Union Pacific Railroad stockholders who lobbied for the park secretly owned most of non-park land.
Sequoia National Park (Incorporated into Kings Canyon N.P. in 1940)	**1890**	Three parks created by the same Act of Congress. All had former commercial toll roads built by mining/lumber interests, 1860-1879. Southern Pacific Railroad lobbied for road construction and upgrade in 1900.
Yosemite National Park	**1890**	
General Grant National Park	**1890**	
Mount Rainier National Park	**1899**	Park area was part of original Northern Pacific Railroad land grant. Existing toll road upgraded by Army Corps of Engineers 1903-1910, and Tacoma & Eastern Railroad ran stagecoach tours of park from nearby Ashford rail depot after 1904. Tacoma & Eastern built the National Park Inn in 1906.
Crater Lake National Park	**1902**	Major force behind park establishment was Portland Board of Trade. Southern Pacific Railroad started excursions by stagecoach from Klamath Falls in 1909.
Wind Cave National Park	**1903**	Cave discovered in the 1880s was subject to suits from conflicting mining and homestead claims. Secretary of the Interior invalidated both claims in 1903 and reserved the land for a national park; NPS did not assume a role until 1916.
Sully's Hill National Park (Converted to Game Preserve in 1931)	**1904**	Northern Pacific Railroad pushed for the establishment of the park.
Mesa Verde National Park	**1906**	Contractors for the government between 1908 and 1914 built the wagon road through the park. Early accommodations were just tents on platforms with very poor sanitation. On January 1, 1930, the Denver & Rio Grand Western Railroad took over concessions and soon thereafter built cabin colonies, a cafeteria and community building.
Platt National Park	**1906**	The Chickasaw (Indian) Nation, concerned that homesteaders were threatening the use of the Sulphur Springs, ceded 640 acres of land to the federal government for $20.00/acre. The Secretary of the Interior established the Sulphur Springs reservation in 1904, to become Platt National Park in 1906.
Glacier National Park	**1910**	Great Northern Railroad completed line through area south of the park in 1891 from which they took stagecoach and boat tours of the area. In 1910 Great Northern built Many Glacier Hotel and other accommodations.
Rocky Mountain National Park	**1915**	Union Pacific Railroad built line to Estes Park, Colorado, by 1882. Six hotels/camps in Estes Park became force behind park. Freelan Stanley, inventor of the "Stanley Steamer" automobile, built the Stanley Hotel in 1909 and ran auto tours of the area and was a major supporter of the park. Union Pacific and Colorado & Southern Railroads were running excursions to park by 1915.
Hawai`i Volcanoes National Park	**1916**	An exception to the rule, the park had no railroad or significant business support.
Grand Canyon National Park (Was National Monument 1908-1919 in which year NPS took over supervision of site)	**1919**	Union Pacific Railroad built facilities on the North Rim; Santa Fe Railroad built South Rim facilities. Both railroad companies lobbied for Grand Canyon National Monument.
Zion National Park (Was National Monument 1908-1919 in which year NPS took over supervision of site)	**1919**	Union Pacific Railroad built facilities at Zion and Bryce Canyon and lobbied for National Monument passage in 1909.

ILLUSTRATION 2: Advertisement for the Denver Rio Grande Railroad Rocky Mountain Excursion (n.d.)

Although the Army Corps of Engineers built roads in some of the parks under Army control, park roads were by and large as bad as those outside the parks.

In 1901 Ranson E. Olds produced the first U.S. automobile in quantity. In that year there were five national parks, all accessible only by train and stagecoach. In 1908, when Henry Ford began mass production of his Model T Ford, there were ten national parks, but they remained hidden treasures.

Soon after Olds began the marketing of his cars they were banned from the national parks as safety hazards, most likely because of pressure from the railroad owners, who saw them as a threat to their cradle-to-grave control of the park experience. But as it became apparent that automobiles were not a passing fad of the rich, and under intense lobbying from the newly formed American Automobile Association (AAA), individual national parks began to allow cars and trucks. Yellowstone, the last to yield, allowed motorized vehicles in 1915.

Railroad companies saw a silver lining in the new technology. Few automobile owners then were willing to drive cross-country to Yellowstone National Park. But the railroads believed that many more middle-class visitors would be willing to come by train to a nearby railroad depot and then be driven in railroad-owned touring cars through the parks. These visits would be faster than those by stagecoach, more comfortable, and less expensive. The railroad barons believed they would attract more visitors to the parks, visitors that still would be dependent on railroad-owned lodges and restaurants.

The railroad companies, however, were myopic. Although they came to embrace the new automobile technology and to lobby for good automobile roads to access the parks that they depended upon for profits, in hindsight it is obvious that they did not understand that time and good roads would render much railroad transportation obsolete. And good roads were on the horizon.

Federal Intervention for Public Roads

In 1893 the United States Department of Agriculture formed the Office of Road Inquiry to survey and research American roads and to educate the public on better road construction. From its initiation the federal road bureaucracy, and increasingly that of state and local governments, believed that road construction and maintenance was the proper role of government, not of private enterprise.

Federal funding for public roads was debated in the early years of the Republic. Many elected officials believed that funding highways was unconstitutional. Others felt that Article I, Section 8 of the U. S. Constitution, which granted Congress the authority to "establish Post Offices and post roads," was adequate justification for the federal trumping of states' rights. In 1893 the U. S. Supreme Court, in a ruling that today might be called an example of judicial activism, stated that the "power to regulate commerce [granted in] Article I carries with it power over all the means and instrumentalities by which commerce is carried on." The opinion opened wide the door of legal federal involvement in commerce encouraged by the establishment of the Office of Road Inquiry.

The federal concern with the deplorable condition of the nation's roads accelerated as Americans shifted from horse power to horsepower.

The first mass-produced cars were made by Olds in 1901, but they were expensive. In 1913 Henry Ford introduced the moving assembly line that allowed the production of much more reasonable vehicles. Soon Ford could sell a Model T Ford for less than

PHOTOGRAPH 2: Road in Cook County, Illinois, 1918 (LOC)

This view of a badly rutted dirt road near Chicago was the rule, not the exception, in the first decades of the twentieth century. Probably shown here at its best, during the dry season, the surface would have been a quagmire in wet weather and impassable in the winter.

$300 and it was evident that the automobile was not a passing fad of the rich, but the future of land transportation. In 1900 only 8,000 cars were registered, but by 1910 registrations had jumped to 458, 377. Almost 40% of the households in America in 1920 owned a car or a truck, and many of the owners of the 8,131,522 vehicles urged their legislators to build roads. [8] Yet by 1925 only 48,000 of the 3,006,000 miles of rural roads had a "high type" surface.

Legislation passed by the U. S. House of Representatives in 1912 proposed the classification of all roads as Type A (macadam–See TABLE 4), Type B (gravel), and Type C (dirt). The law would allow the federal government to pay yearly rent to the states for postal use of all roads at the rates of $25.00, $20.00, and $15.00 per mile respectively. The proposed legislation focused, however, the opposing interests in road development. Farmers and rural residents wanted funding directed to upgrade Class C roads; the automobile lobbyists represented by the AAA (American Automobile Association) and the fledgling hotel/motel industry wanted all funds directed to the upgrade and maintenance of Class A and B roads, which carried tourists and major commerce. The conflict resulted in the bill's death in the Senate.

Representative Dorsey W. Shackleford, sponsor of the defeated 1912 bill, licked his wounds and tried again. His reincarnated legislation passed the House of Representatives on January 16, 1916. The new proposal addressed constitutional concerns and proposed to help the states in the construction, upgrade, and maintenance of roads used for interstate commerce, military supply transport, and postal matters. Each state was to receive a minimum of $65,000 of a yearly total starting in 1917 not to exceed $25,000,000 to all states. Although states would be empowered to select the projects to be funded, the United States Department of Agriculture would review and approve surveys, plans, designs, and costs for each project. The proposed federal share of each project would be between 30%-50%.

When Shackleford's bill reached the Senate, John H. Bankhead of Alabama, the last remaining Civil War veteran in the chamber, decimated it. Bankhead's rewrite kept only the preamble of the House legislation, rewriting the balance in favor of greater state control. Bankhead wanted states to retain the right to use convict labor for road maintenance, wanted minimum federal oversight of road placement and design, and did not want legislation that would encourage organized labor.

The bill approved by the Senate on May 8, 1916, appropriated $75,000,000, with $5,000,000 for the fiscal year 1917, increasing by yearly increments of $5,000,000 until in 1921 the yearly allocation would reach $25,000,000. States were authorized to use the money for the construction or improvement, but not for the maintenance, of roads for which no tolls were charged. The states were allowed to build roads according to their own standards and labor laws, and the Secretary of Agriculture was given the authority only to inspect and approve the work after completion. States were required to match federal funds.

TABLE 3: AUTOMOBILE SALES AND REGISTRATIONS [9]

YEAR	Automobile Sales	Automobiles Registered
1900	4,192	- - -
1905	24,250	77,400
1910	181,000	458,377
1915	895,930	2,332,426
1920	1,190,560	8,131,522
1925	3,785,171	17,481,001
1930	2,787,456	23,034,753
1935	3,273,874	22,567,827
1957	6,113,344	67,131,071
1998	4,600,000	131,839,000

TABLE 4: ROAD SURFACES

Surface Type	History of Surface Type
Macadam	The macadam surface was named after John Macadam who first used it on a British toll road. It was based on the installation of three layers of cut stone, gradually decreasing in size, and rolled with iron rollers.The largest base stones were cut to approximately 3" in size; the top stones were no more than 1". The stones gradually interlocked, forming a stable surface. Macadam's system was first used in the United States in 1823 on the turnpike between Hagerstown and Boonsboro, Maryland, and shortly thereafter on the National Pike. It gained wide popularity but was expensive to install because the stone was hand cut.
Tarmacadam	Although macadam surfaces were highly effective with horses and wagons, automobiles churned the roads and created vast dust clouds. By the early 1900s road workers routinely "oiled" macadam roads by the application of coal tar or road oil–byproducts of the distillation of bituminous coal. Because the oil was sticky and melted and bubbled in the heat, the roads were often topdressed with fine gravel chips. Tarmacadam roads are still used in rural areas of the United States.
Asphalt	Asphalt (bitumen) is a naturally occurring material first imported from Venezuela. It was first mixed with sand and used as a sidewalk material in Newark, New Jersey, in 1870. With the discovery of oil in Pennsylvania and California, chemists found that bitumen could be created as the byproduct of petroleum distillation and by 1910 most American asphalt was artificially made. Road builders discovered that by mixing hot asphalt with sand and gravel they could create a paving mix far superior to that of tarmacadam, particularly if a base course of larger crushed stone mixed with bitumen was covered with a wearing (top) course of bitumen mixed with a finer aggregate. By the 1920s, asphalt roads were the surface of choice for any highway expected to carry significant automobile traffic.
Portland Cement Concrete	Portland cement is made by the processing of clay and crushed silicaceous limestone. When mixed with sand, gravel, and water it creates a hard "artificial stone" that strengthens with time. It was first used to grout a macadam road in Rochester, New York, in 1893, but the road soon cracked and was covered with asphalt in 1896–the first recorded asphalt overlay. The first successful concrete road was built in Bellfontaine, Ohio, in 1894 by George Bartholowmew, and consisted of precast 5" thick, 5' by 5' slabs installed two courses thick. The lower slabs contained coarser aggregate than the upper ones. Portions of Bellfontaine's road are in use today. The Pennsylvania Turnpike, built in the 1930s, was the first major interstate highway to use reinforced concrete.

NOTE: This chart does not include materials used in urban areas, which included cobblestones, asphalt-impregnated wooden blocks, brick, and several other materials. Data for this chart derived from <www.ne.pavement.com>, <www.siue.edu/CCRU/articles/concrete-road.pdf>, <www.spartacus.schoolnet.co.uk/SCmacadam.htm>, and the Federal Highway Administration sites previously noted.

PHOTOGRAPH 3: Convicts at Work on a Road in Oglethorpe County, Georgia, 1941

Passage of the Federal Aid Road Act of 1916 was contingent on southern and western states retaining the right to use convict and non-union labor.

Of no less importance for agriculture and for National development is the Federal Aid Road Act. This measure will conduce to the establishment of more effective highway machinery in each State, strongly influence the development of good road building along right lines, stimulate larger production and better marketing, promote a fuller and more attractive rural life, add greatly to convenience and economic welfare of all the people, and strengthen the national foundations. [10]

On August 16, 1917, American Association of State Highway Officials (AASHO) representatives from 35 states met in Washington with the Department of Agriculture's Office of Public Roads and Rural Engineering (OPRRE) to establish guidelines for the new federal/state cooperation on road construction. As of that date, six states did not have highway agencies and did not participate. Indiana, sued by local residents who believed state control of roads was an unconstitutional intervention, was the last state to establish a highway commission in 1919. [11]

The House and Senate conference committees slightly modified the Senate version. The final bill specifically eliminated funding for roads in cities, and the method specified for the apportionment of funds greatly favored the more rural South and West. It did nothing to establish a national highway system long favored by the AAA and tourism industry.

On July 11, 1916, President Woodrow Wilson signed the legislation. Wilson stated in a letter to the House of Representatives Chairman for the Committee on Agriculture:

Between 1916 and 1921 paved state road mileage increased by 31%. But quickly the flaw in the 1916 Federal Aid Road Act foreseen by the AAA became evident. Although states were building roads at record rates, few of the roads connected with each other to create long distance interstate corridors. The United States Congress finally acted to correct this problem in November 1921 by passing the Federal Highway Act. The law required up to 7% of the state roads that were to be upgraded or built with federal funds to connect with highways in neighboring states. It also required the Department of Agriculture to survey and design a system of interstate highways.

By November 1923 the survey/designation was completed and the Bureau of Public Roads published a map of the Federal-Aid Highway System. In 1926, in order to resolve the chaos of road names and designations that changed between political jurisdictions, and after the required approval by individual state ballots, a national uniform system of road numbering was implemented using the black-and-white shield-shaped highway markers still seen on some American highways.

In a single decade the groundwork had been laid to transform the American landscape from one in which a transcontinental drive by automobile could take up to two months, [12] to one in which the trip could be undertaken in less than ten days.

The National Park Service

In 1914 wealthy Chicago businessmen Stephen T. Mather wrote a letter to Secretary of the Interior Franklin L. Lane in which he complained about the deplorable management of the national parks; in response, Lane brought Mather to Washington to serve as his assistant for park issues. He was joined in 1915 by 25-year-old Horace M. Albright, an Interior Department employee, who became his principal aide.

Mather and Albright campaigned for a national park bureau to provide central oversight of the growing number of national parks and monuments. Although they loved the areas for natural beauty, both men continually stressed their value as cash cows for the tourism industry. They spoke the language of the railroad czars, many of whom Mather had dealt with in his former career and social life, and convinced them to support the park bureau cause. Seventeen railroads responded and contributed funds to produce *The National Park Portfolio*, a beautifully illustrated publication sent to congressmen and other wielders of national influence in early 1916. The publication was soon followed by glowing pictorial tributes to the wonders of the parks in *The National Geographic Magazine* and *The Saturday Evening Post*.

On August 25, 1916, the curious park alliance succeeded in their efforts and President Woodrow Wilson signed legislation establishing the National Park Service within the Department of the Interior. The new agency was charged "to conserve the scenery and the natural and historic objects and the wildlife therein and to provide for the enjoyment of the same in such manner and by such means as will leave them unimpaired for the enjoyment of future generations." [13]

Mather was made Director by Secretary Lane; Albright Assistant Director. The agency gained oversight of fourteen national parks and eighteen national monuments. [14]

It is not coincidence that the Federal Aid Highway Act had been passed by Congress just

three months earlier. Politicians and business had embraced the automobile and saw the future in the mobility it offered. They also saw an increasing source of revenue to build more roads to encourage more travel. State property tax income from vehicles jumped from $12,385,000 in 1914 (the first year itemized by the U.S. Census Bureau) to $356,041,000 in 1930. State taxes on gasoline (first itemized in 1919) increased from $1,023,000 to $494,622,000 in eleven years. [15] Good roads and good places to visit clearly led to a healthier bottom line and, as an added benefit, to a healthier citizenry.

In 1918 Secretary of the Interior Lane issued a policy directive elaborating on the National Park Service mission. Although emphasizing the goal of resource preservation, the letter also strongly encouraged the development of visitor facilities accessible by privately owned automobiles. The Secretary, Mather, and Albright believed that the future of the national parks depended on increased visitation and that visitors would come only if better public programs and accommodations were developed. Those developments were to be built by private concessioners, in many cases the railroads.

In 1920 the Union Pacific Railroad successfully lobbied Congress to fund a loop road connecting Zion National Park, Bryce Canyon, Cedar Breaks, and the North Rim of the Grand Canyon with a connector road to the Union Pacific rail depot in Cedar City, Utah. At Cedar City colorful Union Pacific jitneys and touring cars would whisk visitors

PHOTOGRAPH 4: Construction on U.S. Highway 211 East Near Luray, Virginia, ca. 1925

Early road building and road maintenance relied heavily on hand labor and horse power. The first construction on Skyline Drive was intended to be undertaken by local men with hand tools, but these were quickly superseded by heavy machinery.

to the parks' scenic splendors and to concessions managed by the Union Pacific.

The emerging influence of the National Park Service and its approach to tourism was readily seen in the report given to Congress by the Department of Agriculture, Bureau of Public Roads, as required by the Federal Highway Act of 1921. Three of the newly-designated interstate highways were to end (or begin?) at Yellowstone National Park: U.S. Highway 14, extending 1,398 miles from Chicago; U.S. 16, running 1,440 miles from Milwaukee,

Wisconsin; and U.S. 20, starting in Boston, Massachusetts, and winding 2,376 miles across the heartland of America. In 1940 U.S. 20 would be extended an additional 861 miles to Newport, Oregon. Clearly Mather and Albright took interstate to mean interpark.

National Park Service Growth

A large part of the early National Park Service's influence in Washington was due to sympathetic support from the far more powerful railroad and travel industry. In 1917 the Service had a Washington staff of six (See ILLUSTRATION 3 [16]) and a total budget not to exceed $19,500 ($280,474 in 2005 dollars [17]). Yet this small staff was expected to provide oversight and design services for 39 western parks, monuments, and reservations covering over 9,915 square miles. [18]

Mather and Albright soon realized that the success of their organization was dependent not only on the roads providing access to the parks, but also on those within them as well. Relying initially on the Army Corps of Engineers or local contractors hired by park superintendents to build or upgrade park roads, they quickly realized that the results were harmful to the landscapes the park system was meant to protect. The National Park Service Statement of Policy drafted by Mather and Albright and issued by Secretary of the Interior Lane in 1918

made clear that park roads would be designed and constructed to a higher standard than other highways funded with federal monies.

> In the construction of roads, trails, buildings, and other improvements, particular attention must be devoted always to the harmonizing of these improvements with the landscape. This is a most important item in our program of development and requires the employment of trained engineers [19] who either possess a knowledge of landscape architecture or have a proper appreciation of the esthetic value of parklands. All improvements will be carried out in accordance with a preconceived plan developed with special reference to the preservation of the landscape, and the comprehensive plans for future development of the national parks on an adequate scale will be prepared as funds are available for this purpose. [20]

Shortly after Lane issued the policy, Mather assured that funds were available and hired Charles P. Punchard, Jr., a Harvard-educated landscape architect, as the first National Park Service landscape engineer. Shortly thereafter Mather hired George E. Goodwin, a civil engineer, to head the engineering division. In the early years the Landscape Engineering division was based in Yosemite National Park and the Engineering division in Portland, Oregon, near Crater Lake National Park.

Punchard summarized the ambitious role assigned to the Landscape Engineer in a 1919 *Landscape Architecture* magazine:

> He works in an advisory capacity to the superintendents, and is responsible to the Director of the Service. He is a small fine arts commission in himself, for all plans of the concessionaire must be submitted to him for approval as to architecture and location before they can be constructed, and he is responsible for the design of all structures of the Service, the location of roads and other structures on the ground which will influence the appearance of the parks, ranger cabins, rest houses, checking stations, gateway structures, employees' cottages, comfort stations, forest improvement and vista thinning, the preservation of the timber along the park road, the design of villages where the popularity of the parks has made it necessary to provide certain commercial institutions for the comfort of the tourist and the camper, the design and location of automobile camps, and so on through the many ramifications for all these problems. [21]

By the time Punchard wrote this article, the National Park Service included 44 units, and by 1925 an additional ten sites had been added to the system. The Landscape Engineering division, relocated in 1926 to San Francisco, had hired five additional permanent landscape architects and a large support staff.

From their creation in 1918 there had been friction between the Landscape Engineering and Engineering divisions. The landscape architects saw their role as preserving the natural resources of the parks, while providing development; the engineers in the Engineering division focused on the technical aspects of construction with (in the eyes of the

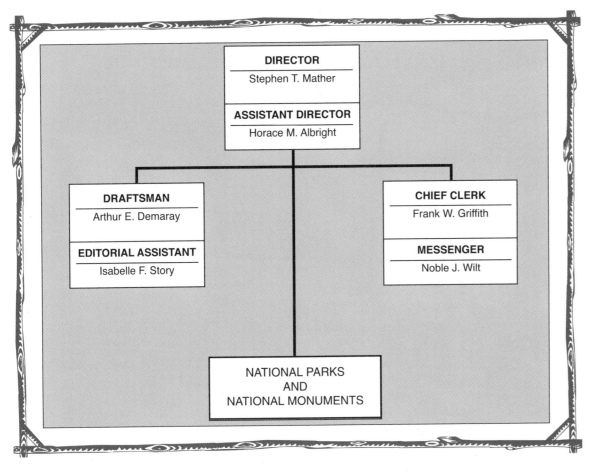

DIRECTOR
Stephen T. Mather

ASSISTANT DIRECTOR
Horace M. Albright

DRAFTSMAN
Arthur E. Demaray

EDITORIAL ASSISTANT
Isabelle F. Story

CHIEF CLERK
Frank W. Griffith

MESSENGER
Noble J. Wilt

NATIONAL PARKS
AND
NATIONAL MONUMENTS

ILLUSTRATION 3: National Park Service Organization Chart—1917

landscape architects) no regard for aesthetics or resources. This professional infighting was of no significance until 1924, because there was little funding for major road projects in the parks.

In 1924, however, Congress passed legislation for the "construction, reconstruction, and improvement of roads and trails . . . in the national parks and monuments," [22] and subsequently appropriated $6,500,000 over the next four years for park road construction. Once assured that funding was in place and convinced that landscape architects offered a more desirable answer to park design than civil engineers, Mather ended the internal conflicts between his divisions. On January 18, 1926, the Department of the Interior signed an interagency agreement with the Department of Agriculture for the improvement of park roads and trails. This allowed the National Park Service to use the construction expertise of Agriculture's Bureau of Public Roads to survey and design park roads, but gave the NPS landscape architects the upper hand in assuring that such projects met their rapidly evolving aesthetic standards.

The interagency agreement was a triumph for the NPS Landscape Engineering division and the evolving design philosophy. The Engineering division was moved from Portland to Yellowstone National Park, and eight of eleven permanent civil engineering positions were eliminated. The role of the Engineering division was reduced to developing standardized park maintenance procedures and overseeing construction projects developed by others.

Congress authorized the creation of Shenandoah National Park in 1926, and recognized that its "greatest single feature would be a Skyline road following the crest of the Blue Ridge Mountains." [23] Construction of the Skyline Drive began in 1931, four years before the establishment of the park. The construction of the Drive is a classic example of the political and economic forces inherent in early national park creation.

"In almost every other part of the country there is a similar need for recreational area, for parkways, which will give to men and women of moderate means the opportunity, the invigoration, and the luxury of touring and camping amid scenes of great natural beauty . . . . They will forget the rush and the strain of all the other long weeks of the year, and for a short time at least, the days will be good for their bodies and good for their souls . . . ."

Franklin Delano Roosevelt, Dedication of Shenandoah National Park, July 3, 1936

Part Two:

A Road Without a Park

When President Roosevelt addressed the crowd of visitors and Civilian Conservation Corps enrollees at Big Meadows during the July 4th weekend in 1936, the landscape overflowed with vehicles that had traveled over the Skyline Drive, south from Front Royal and Panorama and north from Swift Run Gap. Four years earlier this would not have been possible, and Shenandoah National Park was still an uncertainty only seven months before Roosevelt's brief but memorable words.

The desire to establish a southern Appalachian National Park was first broached in the U. S. House of Representatives in 1901 by Representative Henry D. Flood, uncle of future Governor and Senator Harry Flood Byrd. Working with the Tennessee delegation, Flood drafted a bill that went nowhere. In 1924, 23 years later, Congress authorized the establishment of the Southern Appalachian National Park Committee (SANPC) to explore the idea of an eastern national park. Two years later Shenandoah National Park was authorized along with the SANPC's recommendation that a "sky-line highway" be built along the crest of the Blue Ridge Mountains.

Had the politicians, park boosters, and self-described "park nuts" realized that it would be ten years before the President would dedicate the much-

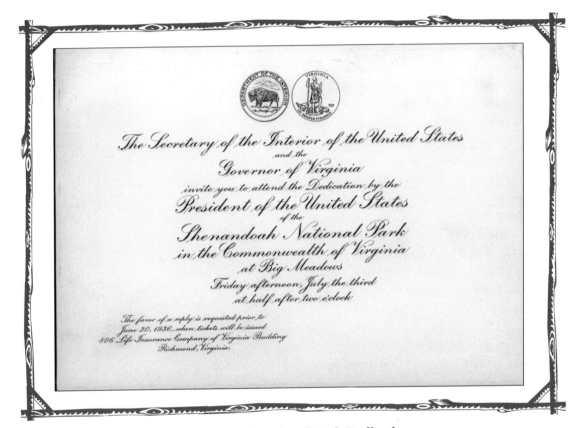

ILLUSTRATION 4: Invitation to Shenandoah National Park Dedication

reduced park to the "recreation and re-creation that may be found here," one questions whether they would ever have embarked upon such an ambitious enterprise. The park and the Skyline Drive were truly born of adversity: drought, unemployment, and the Great Depression were the midwives in attendance. The efforts of the park supporters were an equal blend of naivete, dogged-determination, and creative solutions to unforeseen roadblocks. But they prevailed, and for that today's visitors may be thankful.

Creation of Shenandoah National Park

In 1916, the year the National Park Service was established, 359,922 visitors toured the fourteen western national parks and monuments (see TABLE 5). By 1924, due to both the explosive growth in automobile ownership and the rapid development of better roads and park facilities, visitation had grown to 1,672, 832 at 37 sites. But of that total, 63% went to seven units of the Service: Hot Springs, Grand Canyon, Mount Rainier, Platt, Rocky Mountain, Yellowstone, and Yosemite. Of interest, however, and surely not unnoticed by NPS Director Stephen Mather, was that tiny Lafayette National Park (later Acadia) ranked eighth in park visitation, directly behind Yosemite. Lafayette was the only national park east of the Mississippi.

Mather knew that the western parks were still the destinations of the well-to-do. He believed that if the national park experience was to become broad-based and supported by the middle class, parks had to be accessible to those living in or near the population centers of the East Coast. But though the federal government owned the majority of western land, little similar suitable land was available in the East. Congress had previously authorized the condemnation of private land for the protection of forest preserves and the headwaters of streams under the interstate commerce and military defense clauses of the United States Constitution, but not even Mather dreamed of national legislation allowing the legal taking of land for national parks.

In the *Seventh Annual Report of the National Park Service* (1923) Mather wrote:

> I should like to see additional national parks east of the Mississippi, but just how this can be accomplished is not clear. There should be a typical section of the Appalachian Range established as a national park with its native flora and fauna conserved and made accessible for public use and its development undertaken with Federal funds. As areas in public ownership in the East are at present limited to a number of forest reserves, . . . it appears that the only practicable way national park areas can be acquired would be by donation of lands from funds privately donated, as in the case of the Lafayette National Park.

Mather met with Secretary of the Interior Hubert Work early in 1924 to discuss the eastern national park concept. Work immediately supported Mather's goal and on February 16 initiated steps to create a committee to study the concept. At the first meeting on March 26, 1924, the group was presided over by Henry W. Temple, Member of Congress from Pennsylvania and selected as Chairman by Work. The members designated themselves the Southern Appalachian National Park Committee (hereinafter SANPC). By the first SANPC meeting, 23 localities in Tennessee, Georgia, Kentucky, Virginia, and North Carolina had thrown their prospective

TABLE 5: NATIONAL PARK VISITATION 1910-1924

Year	Visitation	Number of Parks/ Monuments
1910	87,998	10
1911	226,318	13
1912	231,446	13
1913	254,066	13
1914	242,107	13
1915	337,214	14
1916	359,922	14
1917	492,622	15
1918	456,759	15
1919	813,435	22
1920	1,060,375	28
1921	1,173,718	31
1922	1,218,419	31
1923	1,495,635	36
1924	1,672,832	37

(**NOTE**: Data derived from *www.nps.gov*)

mountain ranges into the ring, and SANPC decided to draft a questionnaire to be sent to all areas interested in being considered for national park status.

In July 1924 Secretary Work and SANPC spent several weeks visiting the mountains in Georgia, North Carolina, and Tennessee. In September the Committee visited the area around White Sulphur Springs, West Virginia, and part of the group moved on to visit the Blue Ridge Mountains between Front Royal and Waynesboro, Virginia. One member of the Committee visited northern Alabama in October, but eliminated the area due to the large deposits of coal that would have been lost to development had the area been made a national park. A similar fate befell the Cumberland Gap area because of valuable mineral deposits there. Later in November the balance of the Committee returned to the Blue Ridge Mountains and, in a carefully orchestrated visit that required the expenditure of almost $10,000 by Shenandoah Valley, Inc. (the local Chamber of Commerce park booster organization), toured the most scenic areas.

On December 12, 1924, less than nine months after establishment, the Committee again met in Washington and drafted a report that Chairman Temple submitted to Secretary of the Interior Work. It stated, in part:

> It is the opinion of the committee that a park in the East should be located if possible where it will benefit the greatest number, and it should be of a sufficient size to meet the needs as a recreation ground for the people not only of to-day but of the coming

generations. The committee therefore decided that no site covering less than 500 square miles would be considered . . . . The Blue Ridge of Virginia . . . while secondary to the Great Smokies in altitude and in some other features, constitutes in our judgment the outstanding and logical place for the creation of the first national park in the southern Appalachians. We hope it will be made a national park and its success will encourage the Congress to create a second park in the Great Smoky Mountains.

The Committee stressed that the Blue Ridge site was a "3-hour ride" from Washington, D.C., and "within a day's ride of 40,000,000 of our inhabitants." Additionally:

> the greatest single feature . . . is a possible sky-line drive along the mountain top, following a continuous ridge and looking down westerly on the Shenandoah Valley, from 2,500 to 3,500 feet below, and also commanding a view of the Piedmont Plain stretching easterly to the Washington Monument . . . . Few scenic drives in the world could surpass it. We suggest that if Congress thinks favorably of this proposed park site, a Commission be appointed to handle the purchase and to solicit contributions and to arrange condemnation proceedings if the State of Virginia deems it wise. [24]

Political horse-trading immediately began in Congress, and when legislation was introduced into the House and Senate on January 27, 1925, the bill authorized not only Shenandoah National Park, but also the Smoky Mountains National Park. In a successful effort to gain support from the balky

Kentucky congressional delegation, Mammoth Cave–never considered by SANPC–was added to the list. SANPC was made an official government Commission with an annual operating budget of $20,000 and was charged with reporting to Congress on the final boundaries of the proposed parks and the manner in which they were to be acquired. President Calvin Coolidge signed the legislation on February 21, 1925.

In May the Commission sent identical letters to the state organizations that had been established to receive funds to purchase the properties for the proposed parks. SANPC reiterated the Congressional mandate that lands had to be purchased in fee simple, without encumbrance, and that only when the organizations appeared to have sufficient funds in hand to purchase the minimum acreage would the Commission recommend that the U.S. Congress authorize the park units.

In Virginia, the Shenandoah Valley Regional Chamber of Commerce and Shenandoah Valley, Inc., established the Shenandoah National Park Association to raise funds and to accept donations of land for the park. The group elected Luray realtor and self-proclaimed "park nut" Ferdinand Zerkel as Secretary and hired a public relations firm from Richmond, Virginia, to raise funds through a "Buy An Acre" campaign.

By April of 1926 the Shenandoah National Park Association reported that it had received $1,200,000 in pledges; the Great Smoky Mountains Conservation Association and Great Smoky

L. Ferdinand Zerkel (1886-1962)

Ferdinand ("Ferdie") Zerkel was born in New Market, Virginia, on February 18, 1886. He grew up in Luray, and from 1901 to 1906 attended the Maryland Agricultural College (now the University of Maryland) where he received a B.A. and an M.A.. Upon graduation he accepted the position of Commandant of Cadets and Instructor in English and History at Shenandoah Valley Academy in Winchester, Virginia. In 1913 he established a business wholesaling builders' supplies and timber; in 1926 he became a licensed real estate broker operating the Zerkel Real Estate Company.

In 1924 the Shenandoah Valley Regional Chamber of Commerce established Shenandoah Valley, Inc., to promote tourism and lobby for a national park in the area; Zerkel was made its first Director. When the organization formed the Shenandoah National Park Association, Inc., to collect funds and purchase land for the new park, Zerkel became the Executive Secretary. When Carson lobbied Congress and secured funding for the initial phase of the Skyline Drive in January 1931, Zerkel was appointed Assistant to the Project Engineer, U.S. Bureau of Public Roads, and his real estate office served as the headquarters for the Shenandoah National Park until 1939. In June

1933 with the appointment of J. R. Lassiter as Engineer in Charge of the Shenandoah National Park Civilian Conservation Corps camps, Ferdinand Zerkel was appointed his Assistant, but also served as Superintendent of CCC Camp NP-2 at Big Meadows until February 1934.

Once Washington had made the decision to relocate the mountain families within the park and

the Civil Works Administration had funded the "Shenandoah National Park Evaluation and Subsistence Homesteads Survey," Zerkel was named Project Supervisor. The effort soon shifted to the Department of Agriculture Resettlement Administration, and the position of Manager was again given to Zerkel. By 1937 the project had relocated 293 families from the park area. In 1939, by Act of Congress, L. Ferdinand Zerkel was appointed the first United States Commissioner for Shenandoah National Park, a position that made him the magistrate for all federal misdemeanors within the park boundary.

Ferdie was a workhorse, not a power player. He was actively involved in the creation and management of Shenandoah National Park longer than any other individual. Unlike William Carson, Zerkel never had money and was constantly looking for ways to support his family, be it with a proposed photograph concession on the Skyline Drive, a souvenir concession, or by the many park-associated positions he managed to obtain from his appreciative supporters in the Washington bureaucracy. Assistant Director of the National Park Service Arno Cammerer once told the Director that Zerkel had "devoted so much time to the Shenandoah National Park project in the early days that he lost his business [as a result]." To a great extent that was the reality of the passion of this self-described "park nut" for Shenandoah. Above all, Ferdinand Zerkel was a good and decent man with few pretensions and boundless enthusiasm. [25]

Mountains, Inc., claimed to have raised $1,066, 693.91; and the Mammoth Cave National Park Association noted the donation of 3,629.13 acres of land in either fee simple or as cave rights. The eastern park movement seemed to be off and running. The Southern Appalachian National Park Commission presented its report to the Secretary of the Interior on April 9, 1926, and recommended a boundary of 521,000 acres for Shenandoah National Park, 704,000 acres for Smoky Mountains National Park, and 70,618 acres for Mammoth Cave.

On April 14, 1926, Commission Chairman Temple introduced legislation in the House of Representatives to authorize Shenandoah and the Great Smoky Mountains National Parks. Senator Swanson of Virginia introduced identical legislation in the Senate. President Calvin Coolidge signed the legislation on May 22, 1926. Perhaps prescient of the struggle to come, Congress authorized Shenandoah National Park to contain 521,000 acres, but required a minimum acreage of 250,000 before the unit could be established. Legislation authorizing Mammoth Cave National Park was signed by Coolidge on May 25, 1926, and required a minimum size of 20,000 acres, including "all of the caves." [26]

On June 29 the SANPC met with Acting National Park Service Director Arno B. Cammerer to establish guidelines for the state representatives to follow in the purchase of lands for the new parks. The Commission passed a resolution in reference to Shenandoah suggesting that

for the first 250,000 acres, as typifying the best national park features of the region, areas should be acquired on the main ridge, including spur ridges and canyons lying between them, from Mount Marshall to Jarmans [27] Gap, plus such occasional holdings elsewhere within the designated area as can be secured at low cost for the purpose of establishing reasonable values for later acquisition of other holdings by purchase or condemnation. [28]

Cammerer again made it clear that all land had to be free of encumbrance and that the costs of survey, title research, and acquisition were to be borne entirely by the states.

Following the two-day meeting a press release was issued which, in part, optimistically (and naively) stated:

it is not the intention of the associations representing the three States to pay high prices for lands which have been recently purchased for the purpose of speculation or which are being held at speculative prices. It is the intention, however, to acquire ultimately all the land prescribed in the act, and it is hoped that these lands may be acquired by private negotiations if possible without recourse to the power of condemnation [by the States]. [29]

Governor Harry Flood Byrd of Virginia, elected in November 1925, and a property owner at Skyland in the heart of the proposed Shenandoah National Park, quickly became concerned that the park effort was in the hands of the Shenandoah National Park Association, an organization he did not control.

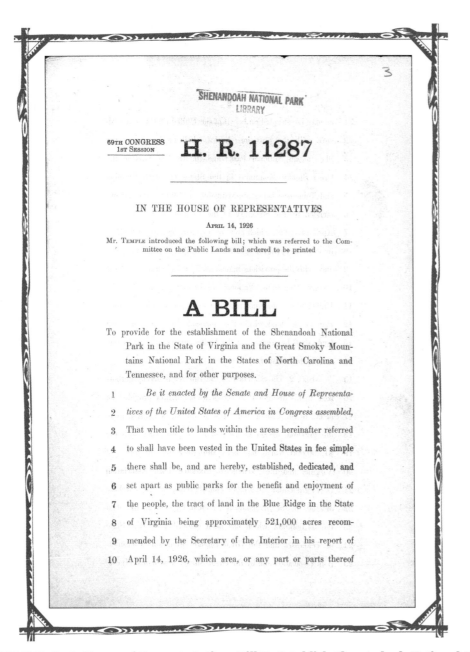

69TH CONGRESS
1ST SESSION

H. R. 11287

IN THE HOUSE OF REPRESENTATIVES

APRIL 14, 1926

Mr. TEMPLE introduced the following bill; which was referred to the Committee on the Public Lands and ordered to be printed

A BILL

To provide for the establishment of the Shenandoah National Park in the State of Virginia and the Great Smoky Mountains National Park in the States of North Carolina and Tennessee, and for other purposes.

1   Be it enacted by the Senate and House of Representa-
2   tives of the United States of America in Congress assembled,
3   That when title to lands within the areas hereinafter referred
4   to shall have been vested in the United States in fee simple
5   there shall be, and are hereby, established, dedicated, and
6   set apart as public parks for the benefit and enjoyment of
7   the people, the tract of land in the Blue Ridge in the State
8   of Virginia being approximately 521,000 acres recom-
9   mended by the Secretary of the Interior in his report of
10   April 14, 1926, which area, or any part or parts thereof

ILLUSTRATION 5: U. S. House of Representatives Bill To Establish Shenandoah National Park

Although he trusted Ferdinand Zerkel, the Executive Secretary of the group, the "Buy An Acre" campaign was run by a Richmond business that was taking almost 10% of the funds donated for land acquisition for overhead costs and financial controls that were weak, at best. The situation had the potential to explode into scandal. To gain control, Byrd established the State Commission on Conservation and Development that was thenceforth to manage all aspects of the creation of the proposed park. He appointed William E. Carson, his former campaign manager, as Chairman.

On February 8, 1927, Carson, Commission on Conservation and Development Secretary/Treasurer E. O. Fippin, and Commission Board member Lee Long met with SANPC to provide a report on Virginia's progress. Carson noted that six employees of the State Commission were working in the field to list and appraise the more than 5,000 properties within the 521,000-acre proposed park area. He said the state was determined to purchase a minimum of 385,000 acres for the park, 135,000 more than needed to meet the minimum mandate of Congress. Fippin cautioned, however, that although over $1,200,000 had been pledged, only $340,000 had yet been collected. [30] SANPC suggested that Virginia might consider the lead of the North Carolina legislature, which had proposed the issuance of $2,000,000 in state bonds to raise funds for the Great Smoky Mountains National Park, but Carson informed the Commission that the Virginia Constitution forbade indebtedness for internal improvements.

William Edward Carson (1870-1942)

William Carson was born in Enniskillen, Ireland. In 1885 he and his two brothers came to the United States to join their father, Samuel Carson, who had immigrated earlier. Samuel Carson established the Carson Lime Company at Riverton near Front Royal in 1895, and William became general manager of the business, which became the successful Riverton Lime Company in 1904.

In 1906 William Carson married Agnes Holladay McCarthy of Richmond, Virginia. Carson's attendants indicated how the young immigrant had risen in the circles of influence. His best man was Richard Evelyn Byrd of Winchester, who two years later was to become Speaker of the Virginia House of Delegates; and one of his groomsmen was Henry DeLaWarr Flood, brother-in-law of future Virginia Governor and United States Senator Harry Flood Byrd.

From 1910-1940 Carson chaired the Seventh District Democratic Committee, and in 1925 he managed Harry F. Byrd's successful gubernatorial campaign. The following year Byrd named Carson the first chair of the newly formed State

Commission on Conservation and Development, an organization which merged the former state commissions on water power, development, forestry, and geological survey. Both Byrd and Carson believed that Virginia's natural and historic resources were the keys to the development of the state's tourism industry. During his tenure on the Commission Carson took a leading role in the creation of Colonial National Monument (later Colonial National Historical Park), the Richmond National Battlefield Park, and six state parks that were developed primarily by the Civilian Conservation Corps. In 1932 Virginia Governor John G. Pollard proclaimed William Carson the outstanding public servant in the state; many other national awards were to follow. Recognized nationally as a "park builder," Carson served as vice president of the National Conference on State Parks from 1935-1940.

Carson was authoritarian, single-minded, and, some said, arrogant. Over the years he had alienated many state Democratic Party leaders. In 1934 (with no serious opposition from Senator Harry F. Byrd), the Virginia General Assembly required that the chairman of the State Commission be a full-time, professional position instead of the part-time advisory role Carson held. As expected, Carson relinquished the chairmanship, ostensibly to devote more time to his business interests. In 1941, as part of the program that Carson had established during his

tenure with the Commission, a state historical marker honoring him was placed in Front Royal. Carson died in 1942.

No single individual is more responsible for the establishment of the Skyline Drive and Shenandoah National Park than William Carson. His dogged determination brought Herbert Hoover to the Blue Ridge, convinced Congress to fund a road in a park that was not established, and saw park establishment through countless delays and disappointments. [31]

DONOR'S CERTIFICATE

Certificate No. 3100   Oct 5ᵗ 1925

Shenandoah National Park Association, Inc.
WOODSTOCK, VIRGINIA

This is to Certify that _F. R. Grantham_

Address _Centerville Va_

is enrolled as a donor of _One_ acres to the Shenandoah National Park, for financing the purchase of which he has subscribed Six Dollars ($6.00) for each acre and has paid the sum of _One_ Dollars ($1⁵⁰), on account of such subscription, copy of which is endorsed hereon.

W. O. Buck

ILLUSTRATION 6: "Buy An Acre" Campaign Donor's Certificate

The Shenandoah National Park Association was established to solicit funds and land donations and purchase property for the proposed park. The "Buy An Acre" campaign was run by a private fund-raising firm from Richmond, Virginia, and gave a ceremonial donor's certificate for each acre "purchased" for $6.00. Newly elected Governor Harry F. Byrd grew frustrated with the administrative costs of the private firm and their lack of adequate records. He established the Virginia Commission on Conservation and Development to take over park establishment responsibilities.

Carson's Commission had received almost $640,000 in cash and pledges for approximately 10,000 acres (to be donated when the park was actually established) by August 1927. But the Commission's six field appraisers had returned with very, very bad news. The value of the land within the 521,000 acres proposed for Shenandoah was not the $2,000,000 first estimated based on tax assessments, but closer to $6,000,000. Byrd and Carson came to the decision that only a reduction in the size of the park, eliminating the higher-valued farm and orchard land, would make the project viable. Byrd approached Cammerer and requested that he consider a smaller park boundary for Shenandoah.

Cammerer spent two weeks in November 1927 on horseback in the Blue Ridge. He rode the mountains and delineated a new draft boundary for the park. His determination resulted in a far smaller, and far more affordable, park than was first envisioned. As a result of his trip, President Coolidge signed "An Act to Establish a Minimum Area for a Shenandoah National Park . . ." on February 16, 1928. The legislation modified the earlier park authorization by establishing a park of 327,000 acres, far less than the original 521,000, but also making 327,000 the minimum, larger than the original 250,000-acres.

Assured by Cammerer in late 1927 that Congress would authorize a smaller park, Byrd realized that the state had to contribute funds for land acquisition. The Governor was the ultimate pay-as-you-go politician. He did not believe that states should incur debt, and, in any case, the issuance of bonds to fund park land acquisition would have been a violation of the Virginia Constitution. But Virginia was running a budget surplus, and after again visiting the proposed park area to be convinced that he could support the expenditure of state funds, Byrd proposed that the state appropriate $1,000,000 from yearly operating funds to purchase land. His rationale to the General Assembly was that the increase in tourism generated by the proposed park would generate sufficient revenue from gasoline taxes to repay the investment many times over. The General Assembly approved Byrd's request on February 4, 1928.

It quickly became obvious to William Carson's surveyors and appraisers that few land owners were either willing to sell or willing to accept the "low cost" purchase advocated by SANPC. At his request, the Virginia legislature passed and Governor Byrd signed on March 23, 1928, an act

> providing the form and mode of procedure and furnishing a system of procedure for the condemnation of lands and buildings and other improvements thereon . . . for use as a public park or for public-park purposes, which shall be applied in any condemnation proceedings wherein the petitioner is vested with the power of eminent domain for the condemnation of such lands for such purposes, anything in any existing statute, law, or rule of procedure to the contrary notwithstanding. [32]

Thus just short of two years after Shenandoah National Park was authorized by Congress, it appeared that the funds were on hand and procedures in place to begin the process of park land acquisition. Few envisioned that almost eight years of struggle lay ahead before the park would be established.

William Carson's brother, Judge A. C. Carson, who had previously been Chief Justice of the Philippines, had carefully crafted the Virginia condemnation law. The Carsons knew that attempting to deal with individual landowners, each of whom could have brought individual court cases and filed appeals, could have extended the acquisition process for decades. The Virginia Act provided that the Circuit Court judges in each park county select out-of-

PHOTOGRAPH 7: Governor Harry F. Byrd's Tour of Park Area

In November 1927 Governor Byrd, although long familiar with the Blue Ridge Mountains, requested a tour of the proposed park area around Skyland before he would recommend that the Virginia General Assembly allocate $1,000,000 for park land acquisition. George Freeman Pollock, owner of Skyland, for once became a primary player in the park establishment movement and arranged the tour for the park boosters. This photo shows (from left) Glenn S. Smith (of the U.S. Geological Survey and SANPC), Pollock, Carson, Governor Byrd, Robert Graves (host of the luncheon), and Arno B. Cammerer at Graves' "Honeymoon Cottage." Not shown at another table were Ferdinand Zerkel (Secretary of the Shenandoah National Park Association), Lee Long, Thomas Farrar, and two other members of the Virginia Commission on Conservation and Development.

county commissioners to appraise the properties. Once values were established for each county, Carson was required to deposit in escrow with the Circuit Court sufficient funds to purchase the properties. Landowners were free to request that the judges appoint arbitration juries to review the evaluations and revise them as they saw fit. The decision of the jury, however, was final, without appeal.

Soon after the passage of the condemnation act by the legislature, Carson's Commission attempted to condemn and take land in Warren County. The effort resulted in Thomas Jackson Rudacille, owner of 685 acres, bringing suit against the Commission in the 17th Judicial District Court in Winchester. Rudacille asked for an injunction on the grounds that the condemnations were unconstitutional in Virginia. It is not known if the Rudacille case was a deliberate test of the new law, but Carson had written to Governor Byrd earlier that "arrangements [have been made] . . . for the institution of an injunction suit and reply to test the validity of the Park condemnation law." [33] On October 1, 1929, Judge Philip Williams ruled against Rudacille, stating that the law was both well reasoned and constitutional. Rudacille appealed the ruling, and it would not be until 1931 when the Virginia Supreme Court of Appeals concurred with the lower court ruling that the law could go into effect.

Even as the lawsuits worked their way through the courts, Carson juggled with the park boundary. By 1930 the United States Geological Survey reported that the Commission's tentative boundary

line enclosed 312,677 acres, [34] less than the Congressional minimum mandate, but more than the Commission could afford. Carson had the unenviable task of eliminating the more expensive acreage in the rich bottomlands of hollows and/or tracts that still retained mature and valuable timber, and substituting the cheaper rocky uplands and second growth or cut-over woodlands. Each substitution carried with it the danger that the resultant quilt of parcels might ultimately not be deemed of national park quality by the Secretary of the Interior.

By late 1930 the effects of the Great Depression were taking their toll on pledges. The national fund-raising campaign aimed at very wealthy Americans and led by Cammerer in 1928-1929 had gained pledges of $566,250, but as of 1930 only $220,000 had been received, of which $163,631.05 came from John D. Rockefeller, Jr., and $50,000 from Edsel Ford. Carson knew that were the minimum acreage for the park again not reduced to meet the funds on hand, there would be no park.

During 1931 the National Park Service sent out a survey team to reassess the 327,000-acre boundary. They came back with a radically different park design—narrow, mile-wide north and south districts encompassing a total of approximately 30,000 acres flanking a far larger central section with about 133,000 acres. The new proposed park of 163,721.46 acres (about 250 square miles) was one Carson felt the Commission could afford and, more importantly, one which NPS Director Albright felt

still contained significant natural beauty. Both hoped that in time, and with an improved economy, funding would be received to make the 327,000-acre park a reality. Senator Swanson of Virginia introduced legislation in 1931 to reduce the minimum size of Shenandoah to 160,000 acres, retaining, however, the earlier authorized boundary of 327,000 acres. President Herbert Hoover signed the bill on February 4, 1932.

With the park boundary and park funding finally in balance, Carson moved into full gear on condemnation. For the next two years the Commission and court appraisers visited every tract within the 160,000-acre area, ultimately setting values on almost 1,100 tracts. Of these, 133 owners requested binding arbitration in appeal of the appraisals. By late 1934 Virginia was in the final process of preparing deeds to present to the United States.

Just when it seemed that the park was a certainty, the government was back in court. Late in 1934 John J. Mace of Grottoes, Charles M. Mace of Washington, D.C., and Robert Via of Albemarle County sought an injunction in federal court to block park establishment. Failing in this effort, Via carried the suit to a higher court, the three-judge federal court in Harrisonburg, Virginia, and it, too, rejected the case. Undaunted, Via persevered and appealed the case to the United States Supreme Court, which rejected it in December 1935. The legal obstacles to Shenandoah National Park were resolved and the Secretary of the Interior officially

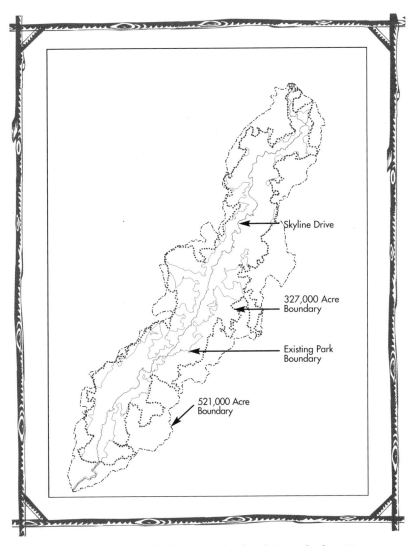

ILLUSTRATION 7: (Above) Three Authorized Boundaries Map

ILLUSTRATION 8: (Right) Charles Nicholson Land Appraisal Sheet

Throughout 1932 and 1933, the Commission and the courts sent appraisers to evaluate every property within the final revised park boundary. Files were created on each tract that assessed the value of timber, type and worth of any orchards, and the construction and value of both house and outbuildings. Charles Nicholson's evaluation, though more simple than many, was typical.

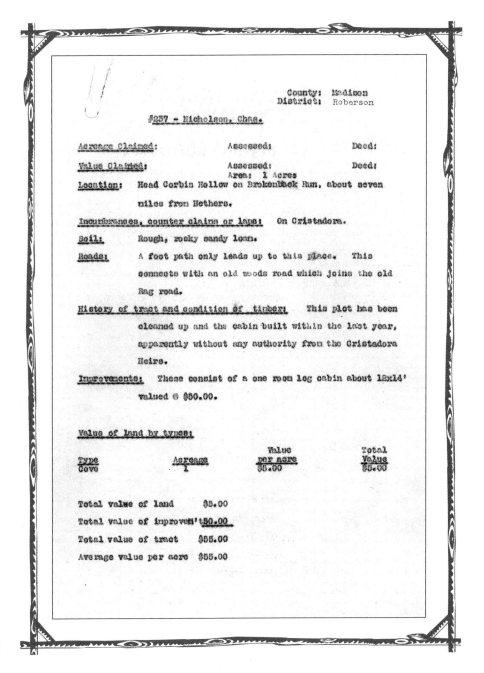

County: Madison
District: Roberson

#237 - Nicholson, Chas.

Acreage Claimed: Assessed: Deed:

Value Claimed: Assessed: Deed:
                      Area: 1 Acres

Location: Head Corbin Hollow on Brokenback Run, about seven
             miles from Nethers.

Incumbrances, counter claims or laps: On Cristadora.

Soil: Rough, rocky sandy loam.

Roads: A foot path only leads up to this place. This
             connects with an old woods road which joins the old
             Rag road.

History of tract and condition of timber: This plot has been
             cleaned up and the cabin built within the last year,
             apparently without any authority from the Cristadora
             Heirs.

Improvements: These consist of a one room log cabin about 12x14'
             valued @ $50.00.

Value of land by types:

Type	Acreage	Value per acre	Total Value
Cove	1	$5.00	$5.00

Total value of land $5.00
Total value of improve'ts $50.00
Total value of tract $55.00
Average value per acre $55.00

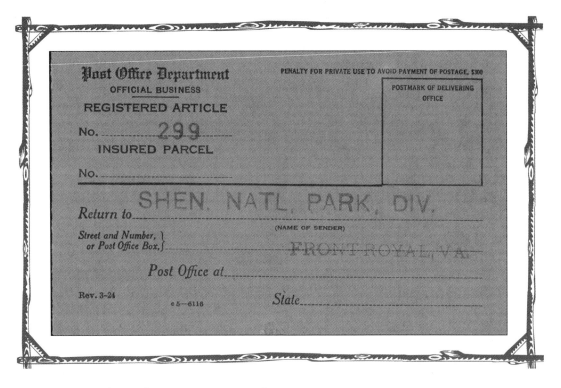

ILLUSTRATION 9: Registered Letter Sent to Landowners

On October 14, 1934, the State Commission on Conservation and Development had essentially completed the appraisal and condemnation process and held the deeds to most of the properties within the proposed boundary. Registered letters were sent to all landowners informing them that the state now held the deeds to their properties and that they had to vacate. A number of the letters were not accepted by the intended recipients (as this sent to Rothgeb Atkins of Sperryville), as some still held faith that pending lawsuits would prevent park establishment.

Skyline Drive four years before the park was established, the subject of the next chapter.

Soon after Hoover's election in 1928, he and his wife let it be known that they were looking for a summer place within a day's drive of the capital. Carson immediately jumped into entrepreneurial mode. Knowing of the President-elect's love of fishing, he purchased the exclusive fishing rights to the Rapidan River in Madison County from local fishing clubs and landowners. With the lure of good trout, Carson convinced the Hoovers to visit the site and promised them a Commission-constructed road from Criglersville and telephone and electric service. By late Spring 1929, the Hoovers' Rapidan Camp was in operation, as it would be until Franklin Delano Roosevelt defeated Hoover in November 1932.

As Carson had hoped, a presidential presence brought the spotlight of the national press into focus on the proposed park and its scenery. More importantly, it made the Chief Executive intimately familiar with the park boosters, the park movement, and the day-to-day struggle for park establishment. The Hoovers grew to love the Rapidan and they came to love the Blue Ridge Mountains. As the economic storm of the Great Depression grew after October 1929, it coincided with the start of the greatest drought in Virginia history. William Carson, ever the opportunist, capitalized on both events to bring about the initial construction of the Skyline Drive, long before the park was a sure bet.

accepted the deeds to the park, which had been in his keeping since late 1934. In the end, the Secretary accepted deeds to 181,578 acres for which the Commission paid the landowners $1,859,910.

During the nine years of struggle to create the park, William Carson was steadfast in the pursuit of his objective. Although Cammerer and other National Park

Service officials had serious doubts that Shenandoah National Park would ever become a reality, Carson kept his eye on the prize: two events between 1929 and 1931 attest to his determination and his creativity. The first was to convince newly elected President Herbert Hoover and his wife Lou to establish their country camp within the boundary of the proposed park; the second was to engineer the initial construction of the

The Skyline Drive: Hijacking a Drought

The greatest drought in the recorded history of Virginia began slowly in the Shenandoah Valley. In 1929 the town of Dale Enterprise in Rockingham County, Virginia, was 1.59" below average rainfall, and Woodstock, Virginia, would have been 2.51" short of normal had it not been for very heavy storms in June and October. By the following year, the drought was statewide, but the Shenandoah Valley was the area hardest hit. Rainfall in Woodstock, Dale Enterprise, and other locations averaged under 18" for the year, less than 43% of average precipitation. Compounding the lack of rain was excessive heat. Charlottesville had twelve days that exceeded 100 degrees between July 19 and August 10, and between June 1 and August 31, 1930, Woodstock had 21 days above 100 degrees and on July 20 reached 109, a state record. This, of course, was an era before air conditioning and, in most locations, there was as yet no electricity to operate fans.

By August 10 Herbert Hoover was concerned. Living at Rapidan on weekends, the President had to have been aware of the impact of the drought on both the local residents and the state in general. He called for a summit of the Governors of the thirteen affected states to meet with him in Orange, Virginia,

TABLE 6: CLIMATE DATA FOR THE VIRGINIA DROUGHT

	1892-1929 State Average	1929 State Average	1929 Charlottesville (Albemarle Co.)	1929 Woodstock (Shenandoah Co.)	1929 Dale Enterprise (Rockingham Co.)	1930 State Average	1930 Charlottesville (Albemarle Co.)	1930 Woodstock (Shenandoah Co.)	1930 Dale Enterprise (Rockingham Co.)	1931 State Average	1931 Charlottesville (Albemarle Co.)	1931 Woodstock (Shenandoah Co.)	1931 Dale Enterprise (Rockingham Co.)	1932 State Average	1932 Charlottesville (Albemarle Co.)	1932 Woodstock (Shenandoah Co.)	1932 Dale Enterprise (Rockingham Co.)
AV. MEAN TEMPERATURE	56.7	56.1	57	53.4	58.9	56.8	58.5	57.3	54.5	57.8	59.3	57.1	56.0	57.5	58.9	55.2	54.5
HIGHEST TEMPERATURE	N/A	99	98	98	96	109	107	109	104	104	97	102	99	108	105	106	101
AVERAGE PRECIPITATION	42.39	45.9	49.4	40.41	38.07	24.86	23.66	16.44	17.6	37.99	44.97	27.44	33.16	44.78	46	43.87	42.02
# OF RAINY DAYS	102	115	113	125	120	86	76	94	92	105	123	106	123	102	99	122	100
AVERAGE TOTAL SNOWFALL	17.5	16.7	18.5	19.7	23.2	23.4	23	15.5	26.8	3.7	4.3	0.5	6.2	13.1	14.5	11.8	24

(NOTE: Data extracted from U.S. Department of Agriculture, Weather Bureau, "Climatological Data", Vol. XXXIX, XL, XLI, and XLII, 1929-1932)

on August 15, 1930, to draft a drought relief plan. Hoover stated the results of this meeting in his 1930 State of the Union Address:

I appointed a national committee comprising the heads of the important Federal agencies under the chairmanship of the Secretary of Agriculture. The governors in turn have appointed State committees representative of the farmers, bankers, business men, and the Red Cross, and subsidiary committees have been established in most of the acutely affected counties. Railway rates were reduced on feed and livestock in and out of the drought areas, and over 50,000 cars of such products have been transported under these reduced rates. The Red Cross established a preliminary fund of $5,000,000 for distress relief purposes and established agencies for its administration in each county. Of this fund $500,000 has been called up at this time as the need will appear more largely during the winter . . . .

In order that the Government may meet its full obligation toward our countrymen in distress through no fault of their own, I recommend that an appropriation should be made to the Department of Agriculture to be loaned for the purpose of seed and feed for animals. Its application should as hitherto in such loans be limited to a gross amount to any one individual, and secured upon the crop.

The Red Cross can relieve the cases of individual distress by the sympathetic assistance of our people. [35]

In reference to the drought, Hoover stuck to his essential belief that the federal government should not provide handouts, particularly for natural disasters, and that the states, local governments, and charities–particularly the Red Cross–should serve the needy who could not qualify for, or afford, federally-backed loans.

In his address Hoover did, however, make a modest and uncharacteristic nod to the economic ravages of the Great Depression. Recognizing that government construction in the areas of "harbor, flood control, public building, highway, and air improvement" was providing one of the few positive areas of the economy, he stated that he still favored "temporary expansion of these activities in aid to unemployment during this winter." He continued:

There are certain commonsense limitations upon any expansion of construction work. The Government must not undertake works that are not of sound economic purpose and that have not been subject to searching technical investigation, and which have been given adequate consideration by Congress . . . . Again any kind of construction requires, after its authorization, a considerable time before labor can be employed in which to make engineering, architectural, and legal preparations. Our immediate problem is the increase of employment for the next six months [i.e., December 1930 to May 1931], and new plans which do not produce such immediate result or which extend commitments beyond this period are not warranted. [36]

The President proposed that Congress allocate an additional $100,000,000-$150,000,000 through the existing federal agencies for emergency construction projects.

Construction of the Skyline Drive in the not-yet-established Shenandoah National Park did meet one of Hoover's criteria for emergency construction funding: the project had been in the recommendations of the Southern Appalachian National Park Commission to Congress in 1925. Thus it barely passed the "red-face test" in that Congress had given it "adequate consideration." Initiation of the Drive failed miserably in the President's other standards because the work could not begin within six months, would take a considerable time for design, and would certainly involve a long-term commitment. None of these issues mattered, however, since William Carson previously had set his mind to the task of beginning the Skyline Drive as a way to jumpstart the establishment of Shenandoah National Park.

In October 1930 National Park Service Director Horace M. Albright wrote to Lawrence Richey, Secretary (and gatekeeper) to President Hoover:

Dear Larry
I had to call up and cancel the appointment you so kindly gave me for this afternoon. Will Carson of the Virginia Conservation Commission was due in here at 2:30 to discuss the possibility of constructing the proposed road from the west into Rapidan camp. As that was one of the things I wanted to talk over with you, I thought I would wait for Carson and I am still waiting. Hope to see you in a day or two. [37]

It is clear that the National Park Service, Carson, and Hoover had been considering the construction of an additional road from Rapidan for some time. There was agreement that there was a need for another road for both presidential security and to provide access to Skyland where the press covering Hoover stayed. But the drought of 1930 and the hardship and unemployment it caused created the justification William Carson needed to publicly push the cause with vigor.

Ferdinand Zerkel wrote to Carson on December 5, 1930, three days after Hoover's State of the Union Address:

> Dear Mr. Carson:-
> The dwellers in the mountains and foothills suffered an almost complete crop failure, due to the most severe drouth that this part of Virginia has known in a century. A small yield of Wheat was had; but, as you know, these small farmers in such locations raise very little of this crop at any time . . . . Canning crops, particularly tomatoes and beans, are the usual best ones, along with the corn that provides meal, feed for stock and some money from the sale of such as is not used by the mountain and foothill farmer. This Fall, tomatoes were very nearly a complete failure, due to the drouth. The same holds good as to Beans . . . . Even garden truck [vegetables] was seriously hurt and some of the wild berry crops that often help the mountain people suffered in an unprecedented way this year.
>
> With their small land holdings and homes in the area under condemnation for the Park, these people not only cannot sell their land . . . but there is no opportunity for them to borrow money against their real estate security- the only actual asset they have as a basis for loans . . . .
>
> The NEED Mr. Carson is employment. If the willing and efficient labor of our mountain section could be put to work at this time when the emergency is so great, it would mean about everything for these worthy people AND the Government. [38]

Either as a result of Zerkel's letter or coincident to it, Carson had contacted Virginia's U.S. Senator Carter Glass, who, in turn, asked Horace Albright if the National Park Service supported building the new road under the guise of a drought relief project. Albright wrote to Glass on December 11, 1930, stating that if

> authorization for construction of the road from Panorama . . . to a connection with the existing road in the Valley of the Rapidan were included in the item for Roads and Trails in the National Park Service in the Emergency Employment Bill . . . it would meet with the approval of this Service. This is in reply to your inquiry. [39]

The file copy of Albright's letter is signed "approved [Secretary of the Interior] Ray Lyman Wilbur."

On December 31, 1930, Carson wrote to the Honorable Louis C. Cramton, Chairman of the House Subcommittee on Appropriations for the National Parks. After an almost verbatim reiteration of Ferdinand Zerkel's description of the plight of the mountain and uplands residents, Carson got to the point.

> What I want to do is interest you in inserting in the first Deficiency Bill a clause that would allow the building of a road from Panorama on the Lee Highway via Skyland to an intersecting point in the Rapidan Valley road, out of drought relief funds allocated to the National Park Department.
>
> This road would develop the most scenic section of the Shenandoah National Park, is about midway of the Park, and is entirely within the proposed Park area. The use of the money in this way would return to the United States, as it will eventually have to build this road and is only advancing this development a year of two. The people of Virginia have already expended on the road that this would merge into more than a hundred thousand dollars, as it is the road that leads to President Hoover's Rapidan Camp which we built in 1929 . . . . The length of the proposed new road is about twenty miles.

After providing a paragraph that appropriately noted than the new road would help protect President Hoover from "an assasin [sic] [if] he had it in mind to murder the President," Carson closed with an uncharacteristically emotional clincher:

> I sincerely hope in the interest of mercy and charity to these good, mountain people that you can insert such a clause as will make it possible to allocate out of the drought relief funds sufficient money to build this road.
>
> In my belief if you do this you will save many lives this winter. [40]

William Carson has been called many things, but never naive. He could not have believed that any federal funds would reach the unemployed or the starving that winter, nor could he have believed that the construction of the Skyline Drive would really help the mountain families.

Five days later Carson followed through by sending Cramton a clipping from the *Richmond Times-Dispatch* (January 4, 1931) indicating that only "4.2 inches of rain had fallen in the Shenandoah Valley in five months." [41]

By January 26th the Department of the Interior and the National Park Service had agreed that $250,000 of the $1,500,000 park service share of relief appropriations would go to the Skyline Drive project. [42] However, funding was not assured until the United States Congress approved the appropriation. It is also interesting to note that none of the lobbying for the initial construction of the Skyline Drive ever attempted to focus on increasing the total National Park Service relief appropriation, only on redirecting the previously determined total. Virginia was originally budgeted to receive $500,000 of the NPS's $1,500,000, with all of the funds earmarked for the initial construction of the Colonial Parkway connecting Williamsburg with Yorktown, a project strongly supported by the State Commission on Conservation and Development. Carson, however, was perfectly willing to cut the budget for a project he supported and give the money to another he favored equally: as the experienced stationmaster in project politics, he believed that once the bureaucratic budget train left the station it would always arrive at the terminus, although there would be slowdowns along the way.

Carson wrote over 200 letters in January encouraging every influential Virginian he knew to write to the Governor of Virginia and to their Congressmen and Senators, asking them to support the legislation, and to write or wire the Secretary of the Interior. [43] Many of the recipients, including Governor Garland Pollard, did so at the last minute on January 31st.

On February 4, 1931, the Department of the Interior issued a "Memorandum for The Press" that stated in part:

> At the urgent request of the United States Senators for Virginia . . . , followed up by request of Governor John Garland Pollard, Secretary of the Interior Wilbur to-day agreed to allocate to drought stricken Virginia, $500,000 of the $1,500,000 appropriated for construction of roads and trails in national parks and national monuments under the Emergency Public Works Act for construction of roads . . . . Half of these funds will be used for building a road through [the not established] Shenandoah National Park from Panorama to Skyland, thence to intersect with the Rapidan Valley Road . . . . The other half of the emergency roads funds allocated to Virginia will be expended in beginning construction of the Colonial National Monument Parkway connecting Yorktown with the city of Williamsburg. [44]

Carson had accomplished the seemingly impossible. He had convinced the Department of the Interior and the Congress of the United States to fund the construction of a national park road in a park that would not be established for another five years to aid drought victims who would receive little

benefit from the construction with relief funds that met few of the criteria established by the President of the United States for their use.

An Initial Roadway: Thornton Gap to Swift Run Gap

Ferdinand Zerkel wrote to his "Friend Cam" (National Park Service Associate Director Arno B. Cammerer) on February 5, 1931, describing the joy of the local park boosters at Congress's funding for the initial construction of the Skyline Drive. He went on to suggest that he was

> willing, as long as I can remain out of going on a salary job for someone [else] for pressing living, to do whatever I can for this phase of the cause at such times and in such ways as I can as a service. However, I believe that I can make myself worth a decent salary, if those in direct charge of the road project will take the view that having a clearing house office here [in Luray] will be helpful in getting the work under prompter and smoother start and continuous performance. [45]

He further suggested that the government might want to lease his real estate office in Luray as the park project headquarters.

In receipt of Zerkel's letter, Cammerer sent a memorandum to Director Albright on February 7th:

I was wondering whether in connection with the proposed new road project something, if only temporary, couldn't be found through [the Bureau of] Public Roads to help him out a bit . . . . If some way could be found, if rental of space in Luray is found necessary, to utilize his office, paying him a little rent, it would also help. [46]

Albright sent the memorandum back with a pencilled note: "Cam: This is already taken up with Bishop [the Chief, Division of Construction, B.P.R.]." On the same day Cammerer replied to Zerkel in a "dear Ferdie" letter marked (in script) "Personal":

Albright and Demaray are planning to go over the proposed survey of the road, which is still conjectural, next Thursday and Friday, overnighting at Skyland on Thursday night. You would not be butting in at all—in fact, you would be most welcome,—if you could meet them there Thursday night and ride with them from there to the proposed terminus near Marys Rock. [Myron] Avery [of PATC], [J. Frank] Shairer [sic, of PATC], and Harold Allen [of PATC] will probably be along, too, so you need not be afraid of butting in . . . . If the weather is bad the trip will of course have to be postponed . . . . This road is not yet a settled thing and should not have any publicity whatsoever. [47]

The trip was cancelled on "account of ice and snow" and rescheduled for the week of February 23rd, according to a letter Zerkel wrote to Cammerer, in which he noted that William Carson wanted Zerkel to "take over the work of securing the rights-of-way for this road." But Zerkel suggested that Tom Early and Fred Amiss, civil engineers already working for the State

Commission on survey and appraisal of the park tracts, continue in that capacity for the road and that he act as the supervisor of a "CLEARING-HOUSE OFFICE" to coordinate activities among the field workers, the State Commission, the Bureau of Public Roads, and the National Park Service. He called the proposed position the "GENERAL UTILITY ASSISTANT." [48]

Three days later Zerkel wrote to William Carson reiterating his hope "of being employed by Mr. Bishop on recommendation of yourself," and going on to note:

He [Pollock] told me that one of his men who works at Skyland in the Summer and who lives in the Hawksbill Peak section of the mountain beyond Crescent Rock had just told him that the surveyors had staked and flagged the road not only from the Marine Camp [at Rapidan Camp] to Fisher's Gap but also had progressed with their engineering a half mile or more north of the 'Red Gate' at Fisher's Gap. [49]

BPR Division Chief Bishop finally wrote to Zerkel on February 26, 1931, and although noncommittal about a position, stated:

With regard to the survey of Shenandoah National Park Project No. 1, we are proceeding from the Marine Camp to Skyland as rapidly as possible. It is our intention to concentrate on this end of the project this year . . . . However, we will not attempt to make any survey beyond Skyland at the present time. [50]

Clearly the Bureau of Public Roads did not envision the first phase of the Drive project the same way as Carson or the National Park Service did, and Zerkel's response was carefully worded:

I am advising no one here of the contents of the second paragraph of your letter of the 26th [cited above]. Of course, it will likely be only a short while until our newspaper gets the information from other sources; but, if the road cannot come out at Thornton's Gap or, as an alternate, down the west slope near the Stables below Skyland, I hesitate to become at this time the one to so inform our people. [51]

Zerkel truly believed that the political and administrative push for the Drive was concern about drought relief and local unemployment. He went on to tell Bishop that Page County residents were upset that the new Stanley to Luray road (the only other road project proposed for Page County with Emergency Relief funds) was to be built with convict labor and that it would not help the needy. Were the Skyline Drive north of Skyland not constructed in 1931, he implied, local protest would be substantial.

By mid-March the National Park Service had prepared a map showing the proposed route of the new roadway extending from Criglersville to Big Meadows and north to Panorama, a plan more ambitious than that advocated by Bishop. The map was sent to President Hoover's Secretary, who discussed it with the President. On March 18th Director Albright sent a memorandum to key staff indicating that the President "was in entire agreement with what was proposed in

PHOTOGRAPH 8: Fred Amiss At Work

Fred Amiss, a local civil engineer, was in charge of the survey and land evaluations for the State Commission on Conservation and Development from 1926 -1933. In the winter of 1931 he surveyed the rights-of-way for the Thornton Gap to Swift Run Gap section of the Skyline Drive and the eastern spur road to Rapidan Camp. He is seen here attaching "flagging" for the Rapidan Road right-of-way.

the way of road building this year." The President did, however, suggest that if a new park entrance road from Madison County to the Skyline Drive were built, it should be located farther north near the Robinson River, i.e., away from the Hoovers' Rapidan Camp. Albright told his staff that it was "very important that this route be explored and a memorandum prepared to send to the White House when the President returns." [52]

National Park Service Chief Landscape Architect Thomas C. Vint and Assistant Chief Landscape Architect Charles E. Peterson quickly investigated the President's proposed alignment and found it impractical. Peterson, particularly, saw no need for an additional transverse road into the park and suggested that it be abandoned. [53] Albright, probably sensing Hoover's desire for privacy at Rapidan Camp, agreed with his staff to recommend abandonment of the eastern public spur road [54] and to expand the Drive southward to Swift Run Gap at Route 33, an alignment far more ambitious than the initial legislation proposed. President Hoover, if not Bishop of the BPR, approved and on March 25, 1931, the Department of the Interior issued a press release:

In this connection, decision was reached to limit main road construction in the park to this particular project [the main Skyline Drive]. Already there are roads just outside the park boundary . . . . and in addition two lateral roads cross the area . . . . The tentative plan to construct another lateral either by way of the Rapidan or the Robinson River Valleys to meet the ridge road [the Skyline Drive] has therefore been abandoned . . . .

While the proposed highway will eventually follow the skyline . . . from Front Royal to Rock Fish Gap . . ., the first unit . . . is that portion 50 miles [actually approximately 34 miles] long, between Panorama . . . and Swift Run Gap. [55]

The release continued, probably in response to growing agitation by the Appalachian Trail

PHOTOGRAPH 9: Skyline Drive Alignment Review Group

During the week of February 23, 1931, representatives of the National Park Service, Bureau of Public Roads, and the State Commission on Conservation met at Skyland to review the proposed route for the new road. Pictured are (from left) George Freeman Pollock, Horace Albright (NPS), H.K. Bishop (Chief, Division of Construction, BPR), William Austin (in charge of survey for BPR), Thomas Harris MacDonald (Chief, BPR), William Carson, and Ferdinand Zerkel.

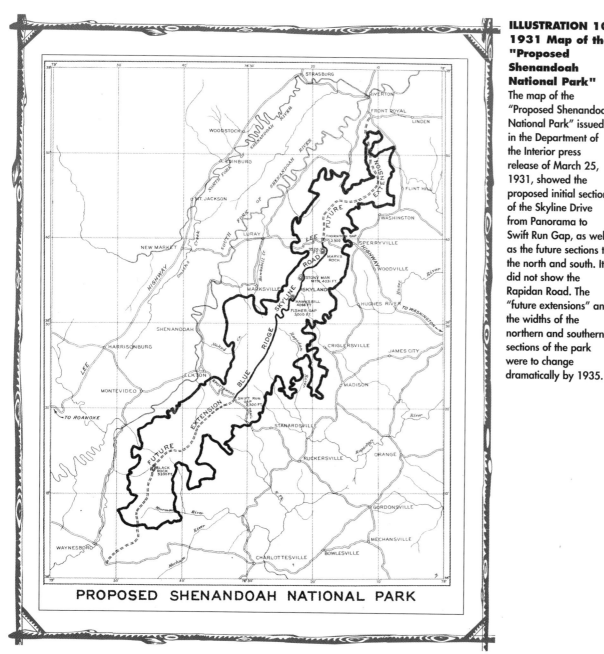

PROPOSED SHENANDOAH NATIONAL PARK

ILLUSTRATION 10: 1931 Map of the "Proposed Shenandoah National Park" The map of the "Proposed Shenandoah National Park" issued in the Department of the Interior press release of March 25, 1931, showed the proposed initial section of the Skyline Drive from Panorama to Swift Run Gap, as well as the future sections to the north and south. It did not show the Rapidan Road. The "future extensions" and the widths of the northern and southern sections of the park were to change dramatically by 1935.

Conference and some members of the Potomac Appalachian Trail Club (PATC):

> The highway system as proposed . . . will cover the park area more thoroughly than any of the western parks, as it is believed logical to go farther in road development in an area where travel is bound to be heavy owing to its location in or near the more densely populated portion of the United States. Further high-standard road developments, however, will be consistently opposed, since one of the major duties of the National Park Service is to preserve and protect the natural conditions of the wilderness.

Compounding both financial and legal problems in the establishment of the park was a basic philosophical difference with some members of both the Appalachian Trail Conference and the local organization responsible for the trail in Virginia, the Potomac Appalachian Trail Club. The PATC, founded in November 1927, had built by 1931 a trail along the crest of the Blue Ridge Mountains that in many cases would be directly in the path of, or close by, the new motor road. At Pinnacles, north of Skyland, the new road would pass very near the stone trail shelter recently built with funds donated by park supporter Roy Lyman Sexton and dedicated in his name. Cammerer was aware of these concerns and had invited Myron Avery, Frank Schairer, and Harold Allen (PATC officers and trail overseers of that section of the trail between Panorama and Swift Run Gap) to the February meeting at Skyland to inspect the proposed route. Zerkel wrote to Cammerer before the meeting could take place:

I have heard that certain officials of the Potomac Appn. Trail Club thought the Skyline Road something to disturb their privacy and otherwise injure the Park from their own viewpoint. Now, Friend "Cam.", I am a member of the Club and have some fine friends in it whom I would hesitate to lose. However, it is a darned pity that people who NOW like the Park Project so well are so entirely deficient in historical information about the project . . . . it seems exceedingly humorous to me to hear of a member of a small hiking club presuming to suggest disapproval of what members of the Sou. Appn. Nat'l Park Comn. in their official report recommended as the GREATEST SINGLE FEATURE . . . . The nature of the Park can be however primeval but its central sector at least must be developed and nothing by way of development can bring the popularity of the motor drive . . . . THAT ROAD WILL BE THE ARTERY. The trails will be the veins. [56]

Zerkel wrote to Roy Lyman Sexton the same day, gently suggesting that the trail club members were being a bit Johnny-Come-Lately.

Having a rumor that you feel the Skyline Road will serve to depreciate the Sexton Shelter, so far as its original purpose goes, I give you my "hunch" for whatever it is worth that the road route will most likely pass well to the east of the Appalachian Trail all along the south part of the Pinnacle . . . . Again, the Trail is incidental and those who have been "Park Nuts" consistently for six and a half years [i.e. two years before the PATC was founded] recall that the Skyline Drive as an automobile road has been always present as a project . . . . I know you have little time to read the

enclosures in full but note the marked portions and tell all hikers the road is a project more than six years old. [57]

The Appalachian Trail Conference and PATC resistance to the route of the initial phase of construction dissipated by the time the construction contracts were issued, but it would return again and again over the next five years. The conflict of public access and use versus the preservation of wilderness and natural resources has always been inherent in the National Park Service mandate and remains so to this day.

PHOTOGRAPH 10: Sexton Shelter

The "Sexton Shelter" of the Potomac Appalachian Trail Club was dedicated on September 28, 1930. Constructed at a cost of $930.57, most of which was donated by Dr. Roy Lyman Sexton, it stood just west of the present Pinnacles Picnic Grounds. Crafted by local mountain masons and carpenters, the design by a yet unidentified architect, although significantly modified as to materials, was a prototype of later structures along the trail erected by the Civilian Conservation Corps. Ever the volunteer, Zerkel coordinated the construction. After the Panorama to Skyland section of the Drive was built, the PATC wanted the NPS to reimburse the club for the loss in value of the shelter due to the intrusion of vehicle noise and privacy; the State Commission eventually did so. [58] One must question, however, their definition of privacy and solitude: the shelter was fenced to prevent the intrusion of livestock grazing in the surrounding open pastures and was vandalized within two months of opening. [59]

PHOTOGRAPH 11: BPR Survey Crew, Winter 1931

Throughout the Winter of 1930-1931 the survey crew from the Bureau of Public Roads headed by William Austin staked the center line and 100' width of the proposed route of both Rapidan Road (then proposed to come as a public road from Criglersville) and the Skyline Drive from Big Meadows to Skyland. Later that Spring the crew had to extend the survey north to Panorama and south to Swift Run Gap.

Ferdinand Zerkel wrote to Albright the day the press release was issued. After gently lecturing the Director on the way in which press releases needed to be written for local audiences, and suggesting that had he an official position he could help in that capacity, he went on to discuss a more serious problem:

About ten of the valley farmers interested in the points named [in the press release] want to meet Mr. Marsh [of the State Commission] and Mr. Austin [of BPR] on their properties and go over the right of way before giving any options . . . . Pending getting these grazing men on their properties and learning the exact price problem, etc. in each case, there are at present some disturbing factors by way of their consideration to fencing along and cattle-culverts [underpasses] at places under the right-of-way. These matters will be handled at the outset presumably by Mr. Carson and his men in conference later with Mr. Bishop. [60]

Senior Assistant Director Demaray wrote to George A. Moskey, Assistant Director, on April 4, 1931, that he had heard from Carson that the State Commission was actively purchasing rights-of-way for the roadway, but that the deeds would not be backed by "abstracts of title," or title insurance. Carson had told Demaray that the properties would eventually be taken in the condemnation proceedings, but that the process of surveying, appraising, and clearing of titles along the route of the Skyline Drive could not be completed by July 1st, the date Demaray stated was required "or the whole road project would have to fail." [61]

Although Carson's surveyors had been intermittently working on surveying the tracts within the ever-changing boundary of the park since 1926, they were not near to finishing their work. The BPR surveyors under William Austin had staked the centerline of the route for the proposed road by April 1931. Yet Carson's surveyors had no legal survey description (i.e., metes and bounds) for the 100' wide road corridor for which the Commission had to purchase rights-of-way from over 70 landowners. The only reference points Carson and the landowners had were the wooden stakes set by BPR–hardly a sound legal reference by modern standards. Yet deeds had to be provided or the roadway project was dead on arrival. Washington officials, knowing that road construction probably was critical to the eventual establishment of the park, agreed that they were willing to accept unsecured deeds from the State Commission.

William Carson had one thing in his favor. Although some landowners along the route of the proposed road were not in favor of the national park, all were in favor of a modern road built along the crest of the mountains. It would provide an easier way in which to get to, and get their produce to, the markets in the Shenandoah Valley and the Piedmont. However, Zerkel's letter to Albright citing "more serious

PHOTOGRAPH 12: William H. Austin

William H. Austin, resident engineer of the Skyline Drive project for the Bureau of Public Roads, lived at Skyland during the winter of 1931 as the initial route was surveyed. Over the years, Austin had many disagreements with NPS landscape architects over roadway alignment.

problems" with landowners proved correct. In the
deeds executed, almost all landowners required fencing
of their right-of-way to protect their livestock (be it a
36" high, four-strand, barbed-wire, hog fence, [62] or 48"
high, ten-strand, #9 wire cattle fence with posts 14'
apart [63]), various types of gates to allow passage, and/or
underpasses for their stock. Evidently residents were
happy to have and to coexist with the new road, but
their demands for fencing suggest that many did not
expect that the proposed park would be created or
interfere with their farming operations for the
foreseeable future.

In addition to the benefit of easier access to their
properties that the new roadway would provide
landowners was the money offered for rights-of-way
purchased in the early years of the Great Depression.
The amounts paid for the 100' right-of-way strip now
seem to have been exceedingly generous when
compared to the appraisal values established when the
entire tracts were later condemned. Although a few of
the properties within the route of the road had been
appraised by the state by 1931, many had not. The
rush to acquire deeds for the road route appears, in
retrospect, to have led to per acre payments in excess
of those that would eventually be awarded for the
remainder of the affected tracts. Some owners were
paid $100/acre for land that later would be condemned
for one quarter of that price. But buried within the
deeds was a contract clause that stated:

This conveyance is upon the further condition that the
number of acres hereby conveyed shall be deducted
and shall be considered as a credit on any judgment of

TABLE 7: VALUES PAID FOR RIGHTS-OF-WAY AND TOTAL PROPERTIES BY CONDEMNATION

Landowner	Paid for Right-of-Way	Total Acres	Total Property Value*	Price/Acre For Total Property
B. H. Spitler	$ 616.00	697	$ 14,161.00	$ 20.32
Blue Ridge Land Corp.	$ 120.00	246	$ 9,840.00	$ 40.00
C. J. Miller, Jr., etc.	$ 100.00			
David & Carroll M. Spitler	$ 300.00	1,258	$ 7,963.00	$ 6.33
J. G. Grove	$ 1.00	256	$ 2,134.00	$ 8.36
I. N. Long	$ 500.00	210	$ 5,102.00	$ 24.30
P. P. Long, etc.	$ 862.00	872	$ 24,535.00	$ 28.14
G. F. Pollock (Slaughter)	$ 151.00	435	$ 1,560.00	$ 3.60
D. A. Foltz	$ 248.00	78	$ 748.00	$ 9.60
H. A. Keyser	$ 953.00	160	$ 956.00	$ 5.98
Sarah A. Brubaker	$ 300.00	102	$ 4,386.00	$ 43.00
Philip G. Lamb, etc.	$ 1,563.00	163	$ 6,980.00	$ 42.82
Saml. R. Aleshire	$ 350.00	88	$ 1,077.00	$ 12.24
E. Luther Price	$ 450.00	130	$ 825.00	$ 6.35
J. W. Atkins	$ 250.00			
Atkins & Ramey	$ 1.00			
Nina H. Clark	$ 60.00			
Charles E. Hawkins	$ 200.00	177	$ 1,849.00	$ 10.45
B. N. Spitler	$ 909.00	3	$ 9.00	$ 3.00
Spitler & Huffman	$ 1,323.00	110	$ 3,469.00	$ 31.54
John A. Eppard	$ 41.25	172	$ 1,634.50	$ 9.50
Victoria Hensley	$ 112.00	215	$ 1,053.00	$ 4.90
G. Luther Kite and Sallie A. Kite	$ 1,575.00	133	$ 1,562.00	$ 13.82
Lariloba Copper Company	$ 110.00	956	$ 3,695.00	$ 4.00
J. W. & T. L. Brumback	$ 300.00	617	$ 14,372.00	$ 23.29
J. A. Williams, etc.	$ 1.00			
Lee Long	$ 2,610.00	516	$ 13,700.00	$ 26.55

TABLE 7 (continued)

Landowner	Paid for Right-of-Way	Total Acres	Total Property Value*	Price/Acre For Total Property
R. A. Graves & Sons	$ 1,445.00	858	$ 10,354.00	$ 12.07
John A Hawkins	$ 250.00			
Ulysses Meadows	$ 50.00	127	$ 1,169.00	$ 9.20
Mrs. S. E. B. Adams	$ 1.00	382	$ 2,214.00	$ 5.80
Burnett Miller, Exec., etc.	$ 1.00			
Mary R. Pollock	$ 75.00			
Homer F. Fox, etals	$ 50.00	23	$ 409.00	$ 17.78
James H. Fletcher	$ 1.00			
Wesley A. Dean	$ 200.00	75	$ 710.00	$ 9.40
Thomas B. Hensley	$ 91.80	220	$ 6,360.00	$ 28.90
Mrs. J. Knighting	$ 125.00	52	$ 1,053.00	$ 20.25
Thomas L. Dean	$ 200.00	214	$ 7,870.00	$ 36.78
J. K. Haney	$ 2,000.00			
C. W. Koontz, etc. (Main)	$ 1,165.00	1,144	$ 21,371.00	$ 18.68
Vernon Foltz	$ 296.00	78	$ 748.00	$ 9.59
J. A. Breeden & M. R. Burgess	$ 100.00	370	$ 3,079.00	$ 8.32
Rebecca Breeden	$ 100.00	172	$ 490.00	$ 2.85
B. B. Burke	$ 450.00	37	$ 465.00	$ 12.57
L. Gruses Meadows, by Commrs.	$ 1,500.00	1,154	$ 6,360.00	$ 5.51
Cristadora Heirs	$ 50.00			
Madison Timber Corp. or Ward Rue Lbr. Co.	{ Timber Value			
Philip G. Lamb	$ 430.00			
G. R. Dean	$ 100.00			
	$ 23,152.55	12,500	$ 212,335.00	$ 16.99/acre (Average)

* Figure based either on price paid by State Commission or Commission evaluation of property value. Some total property data is not available. Zerkel did not record acreage for rights-of-way, but the majority were less than an acre. Names are as Zerkel listed them.

award for the condemnation of the tract through which this strip runs, to be made by the Circuit Courts of the tract through which this strip runs . . . the amount of the aforesaid credit to be arrived at by multiply-ing [*sic*] the number of acres hereby conveyed by the average price per acre fixed in any judgement of award for the condemnation of the entire tract, and the sum of $_____, consideration for the strip hereby conveyed, shall not be considered in arriving at the amount of credit aforesaid. [64]

This example of poorly written legalese, possibly intentionally obfuscatory, actually meant that the amount paid for the rights-of-way would be deducted from any future payment for the tracts through which the road ran at the time of condemnation for the park. Some right-of-way landowners ended up receiving little money from the state when condemnation proceedings for the park were completed because the appraisal value of their total acreage was worth little more than what they had been paid for the 100' wide corridor, only a minor part of their holdings. [65]

By May 1931, the State Commission was registering deeds in the county courthouses for the rights-of-way. Zerkel had been unable to obtain a temporary position with the Bureau of Public Roads. [66] He had, however, been hired by Carson on a part-time basis to coordinate the work of the BPR, the state surveyors, the landowners, the bank in which purchase funds from the Commission were deposited in escrow, and with the County Registrars of Deeds. It was his job to expedite state ownership and transfer to the federal government by July 31st. [67]

In early June, the Bureau of Public Roads had requested bids for construction of the roadway that had been divided into two sections for contracting purposes. Bids for the Panorama to Big Meadows work were due by June 25th; those from Big Meadows to Swift Run Gap were due on June 26th. On that day Demaray wrote to Carson informing him of the results:

> There were nine bids opened for the Skyland section. . . . Albert Brothers of Salem, Virginia, were the low bidders with a bid of $516, 951.21. The Bureau's estimate was $555,000 . . . . This morning bids were opened on the second section from Big Meadows to Swiftrun [sic] Gap, including the narrower road down to the Rapidan. There were ten bids and the West Virginia Construction Company, Inc. . . . was the low bidder with a bid of $171,002.22. The Bureau engineer's estimate was $250,000 . . . .
>
> It is up to you to furnish the necessary rights-of-way at the earliest possible date as both contractors will be getting on the job. Also it seems to me almost essential that the land acquisition program go forward in order that the Shenandoah National Park can actually be established. . . . Here we will have a road completed . . . and unless the State or Federal Government assumes protection of the area which certainly will entail considerable expense, things are going to be pretty serious. [68]

On June 26th, Ferdinand Zerkel wrote to both contracting companies with the low bids for the Skyline Drive contracts, informing them that he had "in hand" a list "of some 100 to 150 men presumably capable in many lines from common labor to those experienced in steam shovel operation" available to work on the project. He also made himself available for any position the companies might see fit to offer him. [69]

On July 5th Zerkel sent William Carson a draft letter that Carson revised and sent on July 9th to all landowners along the path of the Skyline Drive. [70] The letter said, in part:

> The State Commission on Conservation and Development . . . takes this occasion to thank you, as an owner of land on or near the top of the Blue Ridge Mountain, for the co-operation you have given its representatives in the matter of the securing the rights-of-way for the "Sky-line Highway" between Thornton's Gap and Swift Run Gap. The deeds for this right-of-way are being received from the Page Valley National Bank of Luray and that Bank will remit to you, if it has not already done so, the Commission's payment, per the consideration in deeds. The United States Government is being given our deed for this right-of-way land and road construction will begin very shortly. [71]

On Saturday July 18, 1931 (the third and final day of the Virginia Press Association Annual Meeting being held that year in Luray), the journalists traveled to Skyland for lunch. Pollock, never one to miss a chance to gain additional publicity for his resort, quickly arranged a groundbreaking ceremony for the Skyline Drive. Carson turned the first shovel of earth, although Skyland was neither the beginning nor the end point for the construction contracts, and in spite of the fact that the contractors had already broken ground.

Although the actual design and construction of the roadway will be covered in Part Three of this book, suffice it now to say that fourteen months later construction was completed. Bureau of Public Roads Chief Bishop wrote to Assistant Chief Landscape Architect Peterson on September 21, 1932:

> I have a copy of your letter of September 17 to Mr. V. Roswell Ludgate, Assistant Landscape Architect, relative to the final inspection for the construction work on Shenandoah National Park Project No. 1 . . . . We are withholding final estimates [payments] from the contractors until your final acceptance . . . , or if there is additional work to be done under the contract they want to finish it so they can move to other work. [72]

Public interest in the road had been intense during construction, and the frequent visitors had been a source of endless problems for the BPR and the contractors. The previous May Bishop had written to Demaray that the Bureau had "already taken steps for the erection of gates at each end of the road and at intervening points where they will be necessary in order to keep the public from traveling the road." [73] The same day Bishop wrote a letter that must have offended William Carson, both by its curtness and by the fact that he was treated as just another sightseer:

> These gates are to be erected at once and no one will be permitted to go over the road except those engaged in construction or on official business until such time as the park area has been acquired by the State of Virginia and turned over to the Federal Government,

meeting in all respects the Act of Congress authorizing the creation of the park.

The National Park Service has directed us to notify you . . . that Bishop will issue permits to you or any of your employees for the use of the road on official business . . . . and in case you have occasion to use the road you may apply to him. [74]

Over the next five months BPR's Bishop and National Park Service officials were plagued by requests for permits. [75] Under intense pressure from Carson, the local Chambers of Commerce, and local and state politicians, the National Park Service reluctantly agreed to open the completed, but not yet oiled, portion of the Drive from Thornton Gap to Hawksbill from October 22nd until November 30, 1932. Ever the booster, Ferdinand Zerkel distributed and tabulated comment cards from visitors and kept traffic counts during this period. His final tabulation was sent to Demaray on December 12th and indicated that 7,891 cars carrying 30,837 visitors had toured the new roadway in 38 days. [76] Demaray responded that he had "never seen a finer lot of enthusiastic comments than those we have received from persons having gone over the Skyline Drive." [77]

On November 8th Director Albright wrote to Carson:

At your request and in order to permit the public to have a glimpse of what the Drive and park are going to mean to them, we did agree to open the northern end at Panorama to the public until the end of November. In order to do this employees of the Bureau of Public Roads and the Park Service have had to give up their own Saturday afternoons and Sundays to be on the project to give what small assistance they were able to in seeing that traffic was properly directed and handled.

The road will have to be closed December 1st and kept closed until the park is actually established and appropriations obtained from Congress for its protection as well as the protection of the public. [78]

The hardest task had been completed. Although the park was still three years in the future, the central core of the Skyline Drive had been built. The brief public opening had, however, indicated that much work remained to be accomplished. The roadbed was still gravel with no asphaltic surface. There were few formalized parking areas or overlooks. No guardrails had been constructed and there were no sources of water or comfort stations. The roadway was not ready for regular public use. Yet by late summer, 1933, Senator Harry F. Byrd was lobbying the President, Secretary of the Interior Harold Ickes, and NPS Director Cammerer for a permanent opening. [80] By August 1934 the pressure from Byrd was unavoidable. He issued a press release asking Ickes to meet with a group of "representative Virginia citizens" at a conference to be sponsored by Shenandoah Valley, Inc., to discuss the immediate opening of the Skyline Drive. [81]

Aware that political pressure was becoming impossible to resist, Oliver G. Taylor (Chief, Eastern Division, NPS Branch of Engineering) wrote to Lassiter that he should "go ahead and make such physical preparations as are necessary in the way of comfort station facilities, parking places, and turn arounds if they are needed. How you do this will be up to you but I think that to a limited extent you can go ahead under your present E.C.W. [Civilian Conservation Corps] authority." [82]

On September 15, 1934, reason yielded to pressure, and in spite of the fact that most park facilities had not been constructed and there still was no park, the Skyline Drive from Panorama to Swift Run Gap opened for public use. As cars streamed south from the Panorama entrance, steam shovels were busy at work to the north.

Moving North

During the six-week demonstration period for the Skyline Drive, Zerkel wrote to Carson informing him that he had been hired by Bishop as an "assistant to the clerk in the Bureau of Public Roads Office here [in Luray] . . . [and that he] was on the job and [found] it very interesting . . . ." He continued—in full capitalization as he frequently did to emphasize urgency or importance:

I AM ADVISED THAT THE PRELIMINARY SURVEY FOR THE "SKYLINE DRIVE" FROM PANORAMA TO FRONT ROYAL WILL BEGIN SHORTLY. WHEN THIS HAS BEEN MADE AND YOU ARE READY FOR THE RIGHT-OF-WAY WORK ON THAT SECTION, AS I DID ON THE PART OF THE ROAD NOW UNDER CONSTRUCTION, . . . LET ME KNOW PLEASE. [83]

PHOTOGRAPH 13: Future Jewell Hollow Overlook, October 1932

On October 22, 1932, the National Park Service agreed to open the yet unsurfaced Skyline Drive to allow the public to have a preview of what the park would be when it was established. This photograph was taken on October 30 near where Jewell Hollow Overlook would be built, just north of the future Pinnacles Picnic Grounds. Clearly the concerns for visitor safety and resource protection expressed by the Washington office were valid. Visitors parked anywhere along the road where views were of interest and there were no facilities to provide for their basic needs.

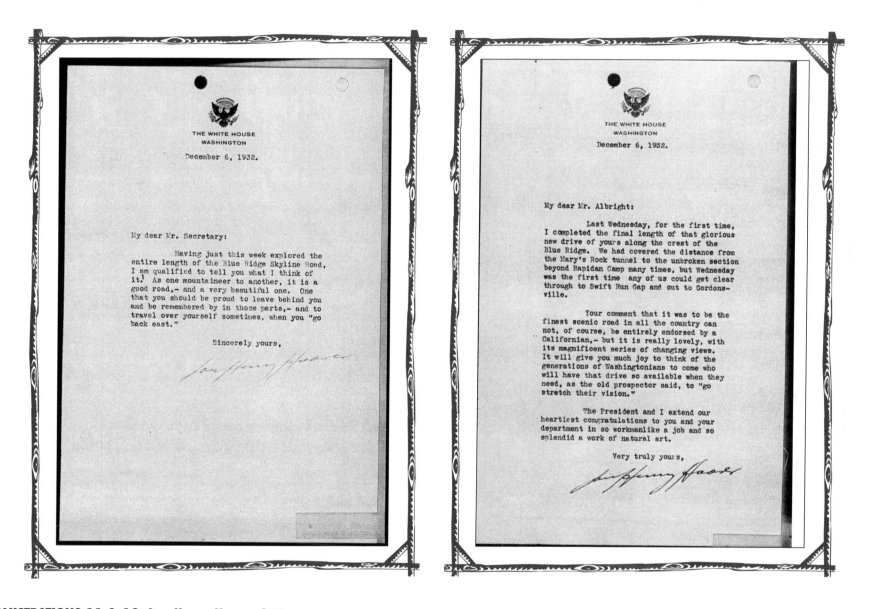

ILLUSTRATIONS 11 & 12, Lou Henry Hoover Letters

Both President and Mrs. Hoover toured the full length of the Skyline Drive the week after it closed to the public. On December 6th Mrs. Hoover wrote to both Secretary of the Interior Harold Ickes and NPS Director Albright expressing appreciation for the new road. [79]

In January 1932 Harlan P. Kelsey [84] (a consultant to the National Park Service and formerly of SANPC) wrote to Albright about a memorandum from Bishop to Demaray in which the BPR discussed a map of the "tentative line for the Skyline Drive between Thornton Gap and Front Royal." Kelsey's specific concern was that the BPR-proposed route at Dickey Ridge was to the east, not on the more "scenic" western side of the ridge. He closed by noting that "the line I recommend is quite similar to the road line suggested by Mr. Cammerer who made the outside boundaries of the park to coincide with this road location as nearly as possible." [85]

In June Benton MacKaye, "Father of the Appalachian Trail," wrote to Cammerer on the letterhead of "The Regional Planning Association of America" of which he was First Vice President:

> I should like at this time to inquire about something that has been brought to my attention. Perhaps you will remember a couple of talks we had (one with Miss James and one with Harlan Kelsey) regarding the "Skyline Drive" in the Shenandoah National Park. I showed you a map being exhibited at Skyland last July on which a line was drawn along the Blue Ridge northward from Thornton Gap and labelled "Future Extension". You said you had not seen this map and knew nothing about it.
>
> Mr. H. C. Anderson, Secretary of the Potomac Appalachian Trail Club, has just written me (June 10) that he has found a series of stakes and markings on the ridge northward from Thornton Gap which

indicates that a motor road is to be built in that section. Does this mean the "Future Extension" that we feared? Does it mean the extension of the policy of motor skyline vs. foot-path skyline in the National Parks?

> I am naturally disturbed about this. Would you be so good as to let me know what is contemplated here. [86]

Demaray wrote to Anderson for Cammerer on June 17 stating that although there had been a survey it did not indicate "that NPS is committed to construction of additional roads." [87] In retrospect, it is difficult to understand why Cammerer would have claimed to have known nothing about the map shown at Skyland the previous summer. The Department of the Interior had issued just such a map in the March 1931 press release (ILLUSTRATION 10, page 34) and it showed a "Future Extension" from Panorama to Front Royal. Perhaps Pollock had redrafted the map in a new format and Cammerer, therefore, was able to claim no knowledge of it. But he was well aware that MacKaye would oppose expansion of the roadway within the park; he also was unquestionably aware that the National Park Service planned to extend the Skyline Drive northward when funds and deeds for rights-of-way were purchased by the state. Survey was underway and continued throughout the summer. Draft maps for the northern extension were in hand by autumn.

On November 2, 1932, a "horseback reconnoissance [sic]" of the proposed route was made by MacDonald (Chief, BPR), Director Albright,

Cammerer, Bishop, Hewes (Deputy Chief Engineer, BPR), Carson, Austin, and Pollock. [88] Albright wrote to Assistant Chief Landscape Architect Peterson on November 5th thanking him for the work he had done on the alignment that the group endorsed. [89] Shortly thereafter Harlan Kelsey wrote to Director Albright concerning the newly completed draft survey:

> I am delighted that you like the location of the road from Panorama to Front Royal and particularly that you approve of the location on the west side of Dickey Ridge. While I deplore the necessity of building many roads in any national park I do realize that in this case the continuation of the Skyline drive from Panorama to Front Royal is a wise project. In the long run, it will relieve some of the conjestion [sic] of the 42 miles already constructed. From Swift Run Gap to Jarmans's Gap however, I am not so sure. I'm inclined to think the pressure is going to be irresistible and that is the reason why I was so glad to go over both of these prelocations and suggest changes and routes which seemed to me would give the most dramatic views as seen from an automobile. [90]

Cammerer wrote to Albright a short time later:

> I suggest that early next spring the entire area from Front Royal to Waynesboro should be carefully studied by our landscape and engineering forces with the view of preparing a map on which available water sources for drinking, sanitary and culinary purposes are located, desirable camp, hotel and lodge grounds indicated, so that a development map for the entire area may be prepared. [91]

PHOTOGRAPH 14: Marys Rock Tunnel Overlook, 1934/1935

Kelsey's comment to Albright on the congestion of the central section of the Skyline Drive as a justification for building north to Front Royal turned out to be correct. This view of the Tunnel Overlook at Marys Rock (ca. Winter 1934/1935) reveals that the Drive was already being loved to death by heavy use.

With the Via lawsuit still an unexpected impediment in the future, Cammerer wanted to start creating master plans for what was then seen as quickly approaching park development.

Another in the endless stream of issues to be dealt with in the realization of the Skyline Drive surfaced in early December as the engineers and landscape architects worked on the design of the Front Royal terminus of the Drive. The original boundary line for land purchase for the park (the "Kelsey Line" and the subsequent "Cammerer Line") stopped several miles south of Front Royal. Additionally, the route selected by the NPS and BPR for the road did not connect with any highways of substance. Landscape Architect Peterson wrote to Albright on December 14, 1932:

> With respect to traffic junctions there are two principal state routes to be considered: the Eastside Highway [Route 340] and the John Marshall Highway [Route 55]. Neither of these has been built in this vicinity, though a small contract has been, or will soon be let from Front Royal south on the Eastside . . . . The John Marshall Highway will probably be the main feeder to the Skyline Drive since it will be the shortest route from Washington . . . . While we are not going to build all of these roads ourselves it seems advisable that they be studied as one problem.

Peterson went on to say that he had studied the state Department of Transportation plans in Richmond "and it was apparent that they have not made a study of their system as it relates to ours." Furthermore, he was proceeding "on the assumption

Benton MacKaye and the Appalachian Trail

The National Park Service effort to establish eastern national parks was coincident with, and most likely strongly influenced by, the writings and efforts of Benton MacKaye to establish the Appalachian Trail. MacKaye (1879-1975) graduated from Harvard University in 1900 with a degree in forestry and first served as a research forester for the U.S. Forest Service, then from 1934-1936 on the regional planning staff of the Tennessee Valley Authority, and from 1942-1945 on the staff of the Rural Electrification Administration. [92]

His philosophy was best summed up in "An Appalachian Trail: A Project in Regional Planning" that appeared in October 1931. [93] MacKaye set out his premise:

> Something has been going on these past few strenuous years which, in the din of war and general upheaval, has been somewhat lost from the public mind. It is the slow quiet development of the recreational camp. It is something neither urban nor rural. It escapes the hecticness of the one, and the loneliness of the other . . . . We civilized ones also, whether urban or rural, are potentially helpless as canaries in a cage. The ability to cope with nature directly—unshielded by the weakening wall of civilization—is one of the admitted needs of modern times . . . . Not that we want to return to the plights of our Paleolithic ancestors. We want the strength of progress without its puniness. We want its convenience without its fopperies. The ability to sleep and cook in the open is a good step forward. But "scouting" should not stop there. This is but a feint [sic] step from our canary bird existence.

MacKaye's vision of an Appalachian Trail was far more sophisticated than the simple construction of a footpath through the wilderness. He saw "the skyline along the top . . . of the Appalachians . . . [as] a camping base strategic in the country's work and play," and went on to outline the four main points of his plan:

> --[An Appalachian Trail] . . . divided into sections, each consisting preferably of the portion lying in a given State, or subdivision thereof. Each section should be in the immediate charge of a local group of people . . . .
> --Shelter Camps . . . should be located at convenient distances to allow a comfortable day's walk between each.
> --Community Groups . . . would grow naturally out of the shelter camps and inns. Each would consist of a little community . . . where people could live in private domiciles. Such a community might occupy a substantial area—perhaps a hundred acres or more. No separate lots should be sold therefrom.
> --Food and Farm Camps . . . Food and farm camps could be established as special communities in adjoining valleys. Or they might be combined with the community camps with the inclusion of surrounding farm lands . . . . Fuelwood, logs, and lumber are other basic needs of the camps and the communities along the trail [and] might be grown and forested as part of the camp activity.

MacKaye saw "the lure of the scouting life . . . [as] the most formidable enemy of the lure of militarism (a thing with which this country is menaced along with others). It comes the nearest perhaps . . . to supplying . . . 'a moral equivalent of war.' "

MacKaye's utopian vision came into conflict with the National Park Service in the construction of the Skyline Drive. Although the local organization in immediate charge of the Appalachian Trail (the Potomac Appalachian Trail Club—PATC) within the proposed Shenandoah National Park strongly supported park establishment and came to support the roadway, MacKaye never supported the Skyline Drive. His vocal opposition to a public roadway on the Blue Ridge crest caused a permanent rift with many members of the PATC, with its president and his old friend Myron Avery, and with Washington officials.

that through traffic must be routed around Front Royal, not through it." Peterson staked out the route that was ultimately used and met on-site with William Carson, who approved it. Carson "declared that he would go ahead and buy the land as indicated." [94]

Before December 27th Demaray had written to Bishop asking for cost estimates for the construction of the Panorama to Front Royal section of road. Bishop wrote back:

> While the plans have not progressed to a point where it is possible to give you an accurate estimate of cost, we have sufficient data to enable us to estimate, I believe fairly close . . . . that the average cost of the work will be approximately $14,000 per mile or a total of $420,000 for the thirty miles between Thornton Gap and Front Royal . . . . I believe we can have the contract for the first [eight to ten mile section] ready to let about February 1. Additional sections can be let shortly thereafter, so that all of the work can be placed under contract before July 1, 1933. [95]

Everything seemed to be in place for the "Northern Extension" except for one small issue: funding. In late December Albright received almost identical letters from ex-Governor Harry F. Byrd, Virginia Senator Claude A. Swanson, Representative A. Willis Robertson (Va.), and Virginia Governor Garland Pollard. Carson had written the original draft of the letters that asked Albright to "reallot [reallocate] . . . funds from the completion of the central section toward this northern project, plus other funds that might be made available [by Congress]." [96] Carson—following his previously tried-

and-true strategy of getting a project started knowing full well that money would flow to complete it—had convinced his powerful friends to support using funds appropriated for completion of the first section of the Skyline Drive to start the section from Panorama to Front Royal. This time, however, the strategy did not work as effectively because some contracts already had been issued for central section work, and excess funds were not available elsewhere in the NPS

PHOTOGRAPH 15: MacKaye and Avery (PATC)

Possibly taken at Skyland, this photograph of Myron Avery (right) and Benton MacKaye shows the pair in more convivial days. The friendship ended with angry words during the 1935 Appalachian Trail Conference annual meeting at Skyland. Avery believed that the AT's value was essentially that of a footpath in the forest, a good recreational experience, and was willing, if not happy, to have it coexist with the Skyline Drive. MacKaye saw the Trail as a means to expose Americans to wilderness in order to transform them into active members of a higher social order—to MacKaye the Trail was just the means to a far higher end.

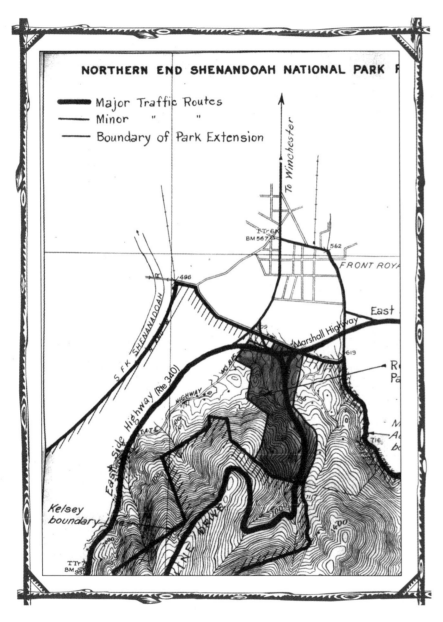

**ILLUSTRATION 13:
Proposed Front Royal
Alignment**

This map was included in
Landscape Architect Peterson's
December 14, 1932, letter to
Director Albright. The shaded area
represents the land outside of the
authorized park boundary that
Carson agreed to purchase. The
additional land was needed so that
the Skyline Drive could connect to
the proposed, but not yet built,
Eastside Highway (Route 340) and
the John Marshall Highway (Route
55) that would not be completed
by the state until 1941.

budget. Carson bided his time, waiting for the newly-elected Democratic administration to take office.

Franklin Delano Roosevelt took office in March 1933, and soon thereafter it was announced that he would form the Civilian Conservation Corps. Early in April Carson met with the new President at Rapidan Camp (Roosevelt's only known visit to the Hoovers' retreat). Carson discussed both the Skyline Drive and the park with the President. He followed up the discussion with a letter to FDR on April 11, 1933 (a copy of which he had sent to the NPS and BPR the day before):

> Following our conversation of Sunday . . . relative to the
> employment of men in the proposed Shenandoah
> National Park area, I am ready to turn over a right-of-
> way on the north end, without any cost to the National
> Government . . . a distance of thirty miles . . . .The U. S.
> Bureau of Public Roads has practically completed the
> survey and plans . . . .

> If the U. S. Bureau of Roads would let this work
> basing the entire project on hand labor, cutting out
> steam shovels, etc., we could find immediate
> employment for not less than one thousand two
> hundred men for a period of eighteen months. [97]

Clearly in reaction to Carson's letter, BPR Chief MacDonald wrote to Albright the following day that

> I now find that we are in a position to start
> construction on Project No. 2, Section A, in the
> proposed Shenandoah National Park, Virginia.

This project is approximately 10 miles long and the grading will consist of the excavation of approximately 350,000 yards together with the other necessary work in connection with the grading contract. This work will be handled by day labor and by hand methods. We would need approximately 200 men and we are in a position to start at once. The men could be put to work as soon as camps are established and the men detailed.

MacDonald went on to say that "by June 15, 1933" they would be able to start work on the remainder of the road to Front Royal as long as an additional 400 men be provided. [98]

This rush for the road was based on the successful passage on March 31, 1933, of the program to establish the Emergency Conservation Work Act (the CCC) and Roosevelt's issuance of an Executive Order on April 5th to implement the CCC camps. The Public Works Administration (PWA) was established in June with a two-year authorization of $3,300,000,000 for public roads, bridges, and buildings. Here were the funds needed to jumpstart the Skyline Drive, but they would not be officially allocated until February 1934.

On May 3, 1933, anticipating the riches to come, Carson wrote to Frances Perkins, FDR's Secretary of Labor, who had written him the previous day asking for potential Virginia PWA projects. Carson listed both the north and south extensions of the Skyline Drive. He also included a wish list of a "Skyline road from the end of Massanutten Mountain near Front Royal . . . to

Harrisonburg," building a "Skyline Road from Afton . . . to the Peaks of Otter [a portion of the future Blue Ridge Parkway]," a "road from Syria to intersection of Skyline Drive," and several other roads throughout the Commonwealth. The NPS copy of his memorandum in the National Archives has inked checks for approval beside the Skyline Drive extensions and an underlined "NO" adjacent to the Syria Road proposal. [99]

By mid-April the NPS (probably because of Carson's meeting at Rapidan Camp with the President) concluded that the future Shenandoah National Park should receive the first CCC camps in the nation. James R. Lassiter, then supervising road construction at George Washington Birthplace, was transferred to be the on-site Engineer-in-Charge to oversee CCC construction activities. On May 5 Lassiter and Landscape Architect Peterson selected sites for proposed camp locations. [100] On May 15, 1933, the first camps were established at Skyland and Big Meadows. All at once the BPR and NPS had a labor force to work with. By the end of October six camps had been established between Front Royal and Grottoes, providing up to 1,200 young men, several hundred local artisans and supervisors, and a growing staff of professional architects, landscape architects, and engineers to work on construction projects on the Skyline Drive.

MacDonald of the BPR and NPS officials soon realized that having the Bureau supervise road construction with only day labor was impractical. They returned to a regular course of construction

contracts, but this meant delays until contract specifications and drawings could be prepared. Although the actual roadbed construction would be done by contractors, each CCC camp assigned 30 enrollees to work with the construction companies, and 60 additional boys were detailed to projects directly related to the road work. The Public Works Administration funds for the northern extension of the Skyline Drive were authorized in February 1934, and the BPR issued a request for construction bids for the first 10.456 miles from Front Royal to Compton Gap soon thereafter. Bids were opened on March 20, 1934, and Waugh Brothers, of Fayetteville, West Virginia, won the award for $427,175. On June 16, 1934, the contract for the Compton Gap to Hogback section of 10.359 miles was awarded to Sammon-Robertson Company, Huntington, West Virginia. The final 10.693-mile stretch from Hogback to Panorama was awarded to Albert Brothers, Salem, Virginia on July 10, 1934, for their low bid of $304,464.50. If all things went as planned, construction on the unpaved roadbed of the northern extension would be completed by October 1935. [101] It was a remarkable accomplishment in a very short period, but Carson had always believed that the money would materialize. He must have breathed a sigh of relief—and then turned his mind immediately to the next project to the south.

Onward To Jarman Gap

Funding for the construction of the southern section of the Skyline Drive below Swift Run Gap was not an issue. With the Roosevelt Public Works Administration firmly in the hands of Secretary of the Interior Harold Ickes (who also served as Public Works Administrator), an initial $231,210 for grading the south section was approved on November 22, 1934. [102] By the following April, the state had transferred the rights-of-way to the federal government, but they would not be accepted until December 26, 1935, after the U. S. Supreme Court decided the Via case in favor of the Commonwealth of Virginia. The following day a $438,475 contract was awarded to M. E. Gillioz of Monett, Missouri, for construction from Swift Run Gap to Simmons Gap. The work did not begin until early March because of bad weather. [103]

On January 9, 1936, Myron Avery, President of the Potomac Appalachian Trail Club, personally delivered a letter to the office of the Secretary of the Interior. Four days later Avery phoned E. K. Burlew, Assistant Secretary of the Interior, asking him to assure that Ickes would see the letter. Burlew sent the letter to Ickes with an appended memorandum concerning the telephone call. [104] Avery's letter put forth a proposal that would

preserve one-third of the Shenandoah National Park as a 'wilderness area' . . . [by having the Drive] leave the ridge at Swift Run Gap, the southern limit of the present road construction, or at Simmons Gap, the southern limit of the road construction for which contracts have been tendered, and skirt the west slope of the southern section of the park . . . . This plan, which would leave the southern third of the Shenandoah National Park a wilderness area, free from road development, is to our mind, one of the most far-reaching proposals affecting the future of this park. The Drive can always be built later on the crest, if desired; once built, it is there for all times. [105]

The Secretary responded on February 6th, noting that he had discussed the issue with Cammerer and that he was "looking further into the matter." The same day BPR's William Austin was told to "do no further work on" the Skyline Drive south of Simmons Gap. [106] Demaray prepared a long memorandum for Cammerer detailing the status of the Skyline Drive planning. He noted that the construction plans and specifications for the 9.96 miles from Simmons Gap to Browns Gap were completed and that the Bureau of Public Roads was ready to advertise for bids. As for the remaining seventeen miles to Jarman Gap, he indicated that "the [survey] line had been projected and location lines staked." Beyond Jarman Gap [the southern limit of Shenandoah National Park] "the Shenandoah-Great Smoky Mountain Parkway [the Blue Ridge Parkway] was advertised and bids were opened on November 11, 1935. The award was made to R. E. Mills in the amount of $322,865" to build the 8.496 miles to Rockfish Gap. [107] Demaray closed his

memorandum by noting:

The topography of the southern section of Shenandoah National Park limits the location of the drive to the present high altitude. Any alternate location bringing the drive down to the base of the mountains would necessarily extend beyond the present limits of the Park, and would cause unlimited delays by reason of the adverse [i.e., expensive] property holdings involved. [108]

Demaray's argument convinced Ickes and on March 3, 1936, the Bureau of Public Roads advertised for bids for the 9.82 miles of construction from Simmons Gap to Browns Gap. [109] The contract was awarded on April 16th, again to M.E. Gillioz. Brown Gaps to Blackrock Gap was awarded to Chandler Brothers of Virgilina, Virginia, on January 30, 1937 and construction of the final 9.389 miles to Jarman Gap was awarded to Albert Brothers, Salem, Virginia, on November 22, 1937. By March of 1938 the grading and stone surfacing were almost complete to Blackrock Gap and the Skyline Drive was close to being a reality.

The Blue Ridge Parkway

Although the construction of the larger Blue Ridge Parkway is beyond the scope of this book, the 8.495 miles of the Skyline Drive north of Rockfish Gap must be discussed. This stretch of road began, in fact, as part of the Shenandoah-

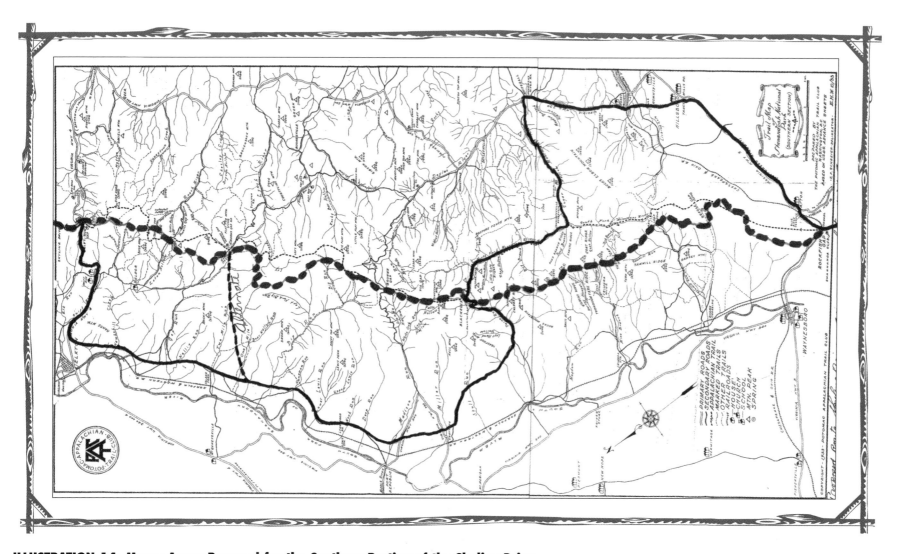

ILLUSTRATION 14: Myron Avery Proposal for the Southern Portion of the Skyline Drive

Myron Avery's proposed realignment of the Skyline Drive included in his January 9, 1936, letter to Secretary of the Interior Ickes. The proposed route would have taken the roadway to the west at Swift Run Gap to Elkton, south to Grottoes, over the mountain ridge again to Whitehall, and then south and southwest to Rockfish Gap. An alternate plan would have taken the Skyline Drive west from Simmons Gap (as that section of roadway was under contract) to meet the same proposed alignment. Avery's proposal would have almost doubled the required road construction and significantly increased the cost of land acquisition because much of the route he proposed was outside of the agreed-upon park boundary. (The present Skyline Drive is shown in a heavy dashed line; Avery's proposal as a solid line. Original Avery lines and the Skyline Drive route redrawn by author.)

Great Smoky Mountains Parkway (renamed the Blue Ridge Parkway on February 6, 1936 [110]), and the design, although discussed in Part Three, reflects its different origin.

The boundary of the reduced 327,000-acre Shenandoah National Park as surveyed by Cammerer and approved by Congress in February 16, 1928, stopped eight miles north of Rockfish Gap. The southern "proposed extension" of Skyline Drive as shown on the 1931 press release maps issued by the Department of the Interior revealed that the roadway would end in a cul-de-sac, since there was no eastern or western roadway to which the Skyline Drive could connect. Charles Peterson, Assistant Chief Landscape Architect, wrote to Cammerer on November 1, 1932, asking why surveys and land acquisition were not continuing through to Rockfish. Albright answered Peterson on November 12th:

> In regards to your question as to how we reach the main highway at Rock Fish Gap when the boundary of the park reaches only to Jarmans Gap. Mr. Cammerer has stated that checking would show you that the area south of Beagle Gap, which is south of Jarmans Gap, is covered with estates such as that of Tom [actually Frederic] Scott of Richmond which precludes going straight through to Rock Fish Gap. In further commenting Mr. Cammerer states: "Topography also would prevent a road through that section . . . . Whatever is necessary to be done in that section to have a new [east or west] road put through by the State . . . will be furnished, I am confident." [111]

The fact that Albright mentioned Scott in particular is revealing. Principal partner of Scott & Stringfellow Bankers & Brokers of Richmond, Virginia, Scott was the owner of Royal Orchards, the elaborate 4,000-acre Afton summer estate that spanned the crest of the Blue Ridge Mountains directly in the path of the proposed Skyline Drive. When Cammerer was surveying the reduced park boundary from November 1927-April 1928, Frederic Scott gave a formal dinner at his home to honor Secretary of the Interior Hubert Work, an event to which Cammerer was also invited. The guests included Governor Byrd, Congressman Temple, Col. U. S. Grant, William Showalter of the National Geographic Society, Virginia's Lieutenant Governor, the Speaker of the Virginia House of Delegates, the President of the Virginia Chamber of Commerce, William Carson, and the members of the Richmond Committee of the Shenandoah National Park Fund. [112] Although the dinner was ostensibly to indicate support for the park, Scott made his point that he had wealthy and powerful friends, friends willing to raise funds for and support the proposed park. Cammerer completed the smaller boundary line in April, and the park and the Skyline Drive stopped safely short of Royal Orchards. [113] It is understandable that in 1928–with funding for the park running short of what was needed and the future of Shenandoah in doubt–Cammerer would not have wanted to alienate Richmond's rich and powerful. It is less certain why in 1932, with funds for the smaller park in hand, he refused to deal with the Scott property.

William Carson, however, dared to go where Cammerer feared to tread. On May 3, 1933, he included in his request to Frances Perkins, Roosevelt's new Secretary of Labor, the request for funding to build another skyline road from Afton to the Peaks of Otter, 100 miles to the south. Carson was always a visionary, and this was the first step in the construction of the Blue Ridge Parkway to connect Shenandoah National Park with Great Smoky Mountains National Park 400 miles to the south. President Roosevelt endorsed the parkway concept on his visit to the Shenandoah National Park Civilian Conservation Corps camps in August 1933, and Carson set to work acquiring rights-of-way.

The proposed connector road was a parkway and not a park road. But having learned from the limitations imposed by the 100' rights-of-way for the Skyline Drive, the National Park Service and Bureau of Public Roads wanted Carson to purchase a 1,000' right-of-way. The first test was Scott's Royal Orchard. The result was the fee simple purchase of a 200' right-of-way (under threat of condemnation) and a donated 800' wide scenic easement providing that no development would occur within the easement area. In return for the donated easement, Scott bargained for the shifting of the proposed route from the crest of the Blue Ridge (where it would impact the view from his country house) to the western slope of the mountain where he and his guests would not see the roadway. The 200' right-of-way with associated easements became the norm for the balance of the Blue Ridge Parkway. Parkway Resident Landscape Architect Stanley W. Abbott wrote Thomas Vint, Chief Architect of the NPS, in November 1936:

The State of Virginia is unwilling to consider purchase of additional fee simple land in lieu of scenic easements except in those few cases where they have not yet reached an agreement with property owners. [114]

But the rights-of-way to the Jarman Gap to Rockfish Gap portion of the Parkway had been turned over and the contract for construction had been awarded on November 11, 1935.

One small problem remained. The eight miles of proposed Parkway would not connect with east/west State Route # 250 at Rockfish Gap and no rights-of-way had been obtained for the connection. The private Swannanoa Club, a large landowner, owned the site of the proposed connector road. On April 10, 1937, Chief Architect Vint wrote to Stanley Abbott that H. G. Shirley, Commissioner of the Virginia Department of Highways, had telephoned Demaray and stated that

it would be necessary to acquire the desirable right-of-way by condemnation from the Swannanoa Club and that the State would prefer to make the condemnation on the basis of the total land which would be acquired from the Swannanoa Club in the entire distance that the parkway traverses land under their ownership. This would involve the determination of parkway land requirements south of Rockfish Gap for a distance of about one mile or two. [115]

Although the National Park Service planned only to design a temporary connector road to Route # 250, the Virginia Department of Transportation purchased rights-of-way to the south with a future

cloverleaf intersection in mind. On June 3, 1939, with construction almost complete, Demaray gave the Superintendent of Shenandoah National Park "full authority to administer the Parkway lands between Jarmans Gap and Rockfish Gap." [116]

The U. S. House of Representatives' Committee on Appropriations, with agreement from Secretary Ickes, in a period of fiscal austerity, required that visitors to the Skyline Drive pay an entrance fee of 25 cents per car as of May 1939. The toll was not supported by the National Park Service and was deeply resented in the Commonwealth of Virginia, which had, after all, donated the rights-of-way for the Skyline Drive. But the fee was retained in spite of editorial pressure and public outcry.

On August 29, 1939, the southern section of the Skyline Drive and the northern end of the Blue Ridge Parkway were opened to the public. After fifteen years it was possible to drive from Front Royal to Rockfish Gap on the scenic mountain roadway, flanked by mountain laurel and dogwood, enjoying vistas east and west and stopping on well-designed overlooks and parking areas.

William Carson, perhaps, best summed up the effort in his 1934 report to the State Commission at the time of his stepping down as Chairman:

ALL IS WELL THAT ENDS WELL . . . and our report is that the lands within the park area have been purchased and paid for; that deeds have been made to the national government and are in the hands of the

Secretary of the Interior; that the skyline drive is more than two-thirds completed and that through the diligence, forethought and energy of the commission the park is advanced ...in its development and that it is one of the greatest beauty spots in the United States. [117]

The beauty seen by the early visitors to the Skyline Drive, however, was not of nature's creation. It was the carefully designed product of the engineers, architects, and landscape architects of the Bureau of Public Roads, the National Park Service, and the Civilian Conservation Corps. In creating the first major National Park Service road in the East, they were developing and testing aesthetic standards that would long be considered the best of road design.

PHOTOGRAPH 16: Mr. and Mrs. J. C. Jensen

Mr. and Mrs. J. C. Jensen of Greenport, Long Island, New York, were the first visitors to pay the 25-cent entrance fee to the Skyline Drive in May 1939.

"The Public Roads Administration, using funds allotted to the National Park Service, has surveyed our road routes and planned and constructed our major roads. This arrangement has been a happy one. They furnish us with road construction knowledge. We add to that the specialized skill of our experts in protecting valuable scenes. The result we feel is the presentation of unusual natural [118] areas to the visiting public who takes for granted the ease at which they reach the formerly inaccessible places or reach exceptional views of them."

Thomas J. Allen, NPS Regional Director for Region One [119]

Part Three:

The Skyline Drive As Landscape Design

Aligning the Road

On June 27, 1931, the day after bids were opened for construction of the first section of the Skyline Drive, Acting NPS Director Demaray wrote to Gilmore D. Clarke (Fellow, American Society of Landscape Architects) asking him to come to the Blue Ridge to evaluate the project. Clarke wrote on July 6th that he was not able to visit the park in the next few months, but that he had reviewed the plans at the Bureau of Public Roads with Chief of Construction Bishop in Washington the previous week. Clarke was not gentle in his comments:

[I was] surprised to find that the alignment was typical of what the highway engineer has been accustomed to do. While the plans were, I believe, approved by a representative of your landscape department, they showed that no attention whatever had been given to the refinements of alignment which should obtain on a road or drive in our National Parks. I fully realize that the work was of necessity accomplished in a very short time. The basic layout is doubtless satisfactory, and naturally I have every confidence in Mr. Bishop and his associates to place the road in the best possible location with respect to grades and so as not to destroy any more of the natural features of the terrain than absolutely necessary. However, without altering the general location, and I believe

without increasing the quantities of excavation and fill, the alignment could be materially improved upon. This is the contribution which the landscape architect, experienced in road planning, could have made . . . . The chief criticism is that the line has been too mechanically laid down—the artistry of road planning is lacking and therefore it is not of National Park quality. [120]

Demaray sent Clarke's letter on to NPS Assistant Landscape Architect Charles Peterson. Peterson was the "representative of . . . the landscape department" who had signed off on the drawings on June 9, 1931, and naturally was defensive in his response:

While it would appear in the letter that the landscape architects had failed to fulfill their normal function of insisting on proper design, I am persuaded that the situation cannot be so simple and easily defined. It is true that I signed the title sheet which nominally approves the plans and specifications for the work and that this was done before I had ever seen the plans, which at the time were being completed under great stress . . . . In the light of the mountain road surveys which I have been concerned with and using the location policies of the Bureau of Public Roads as practiced in the West as a basic premise, the line I inspected seemed to me to be well laid out . . . . If this road is not well laid out, then we have no good roads in the western Parks. I would hesitate to make such an

indictment, because I believe the Landscape Division of the Park Service has had much more experience on this mountain type of work than all of the other landscape offices which have ever existed in this country . . . . There remains the matter of how much can be done to improve the line as it now stands. To put in the so-called "landscape improvements" . . . it will be necessary to plot the roadside topography . . . . Only in this way will the road ultimately be fitted to the country . . . . If the Bureau is willing to "spiral" into curves . . . that is fine from the landscape standpoint. So far as I know, it has not been done previously in our western work. [121]

Peterson also noted in his letter that, in order for BPR's work on the Skyline Drive to be supervised effectively by the National Park Service, he needed two additional landscape architects in his office.

The problems with the initial plans had several causes: foremost was the severe limitation imposed by the narrow (100') right-of-way purchased by Carson. Peterson did not have adequate staff to review and closely supervise work of the Skyline Drive; the Bureau of Public Roads' engineers judged the success of road placement and alignment by vastly different criteria than did landscape architects.

Nothing could be done about the right-of-way. Until the park was established in late 1935, the

Charles Peterson (1906-2004)

Charles E. Peterson graduated in 1928 from the University of Minnesota with a degree in architecture. He accepted a position as a rod man (a secondary surveyor position) with the Bureau of Public Roads and spent two seasons working in the West. In January 1929 he accepted a position as an architect and landscape architect [122] with the National Park Service Landscape Division in San Francisco, supervised by Chief Landscape Architect Thomas C. Vint. In 1930, following what Vint believed should be the normal sequence in professional development, Peterson was moved out of the San Francisco office to the new position of Assistant Chief Landscape Architect, heading the new Eastern Office headquartered in Yorktown, Virginia. Peterson's initial professional staff in Yorktown consisted only of Assistant Landscape Architect Roswell Ludgate.

Peterson first worked on the restoration of Yorktown's Moore House, the site of the British surrender, and on the plans for the Colonial Parkway connecting Williamsburg with Yorktown. In 1933 Peterson proposed the creation of the Historic American Buildings Survey (HABS) as a New Deal program to create jobs for unemployed architects,

draftsmen, and photographers, a program that to this date has documented over 35,000 historic structures.

William Austin, Engineer of Construction for the Bureau of Public Roads for the Skyline Drive, had employed Peterson during the summer of 1928 in the survey of the General's Highway leading to the General Grant sequoia tree in Sequoia National Park. Thus when Peterson was called to help plot the path of the proposed road in Shenandoah National Park, he would be working with an old friend. Peterson has written:

> In the new Shenandoah Park Austin and I flagged out the line for the Skyline Drive's north two thirds foot by foot—maybe sixty miles . . . . The overall idea was that motorists should be able to drive out of Washington for a Sunday's mountain experience and get back home by night. By holding the speed down it was possible to follow the rugged topography without tearing up the scenery too much. Only one short tunnel was necessary. It would be the first national park to be visited by many Easterners and it became very popular. [123]

Peterson was actively involved in most architectural and landscape design decisions affecting the Skyline Drive and Shenandoah National Park. He, probably more than any other landscape professional, is responsible for the overall product.

In the early 1950s Peterson became the historic architect for Independence National Historical Park and was responsible for the restoration of many of the buildings in Philadelphia's Society Hill. He retired from the NPS in 1962, but continued to work in the field of historic preservation until his death in 2004. [124]

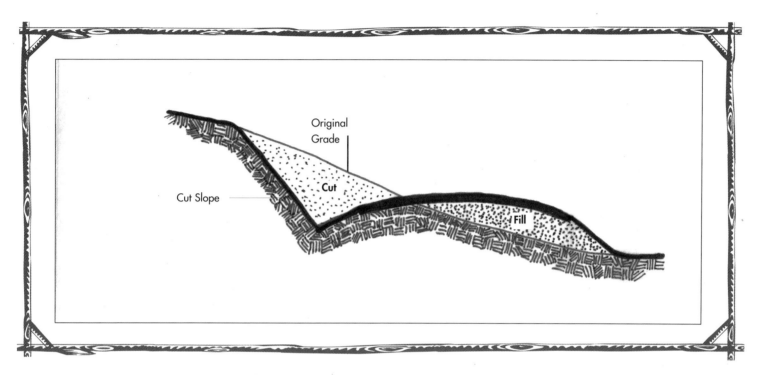

designers had to work within the narrow band of mountain ridges as best they could. Design flaws could be corrected when more land was available. Peterson's staff would not be enlarged until the Civilian Conservation Corps was created and the National Park Service had adequate funds to establish the first two resident landscape architect positions for the Skyline Drive project. The professional conflicts were an issue that never would be fully resolved, and in fact, one that continues to this day. To a great extent, it stems from how practitioners of each discipline approach road design.

At the risk of gross oversimplification, it may be said that engineers approach road design as a

mathematical exercise, and landscape architects as a canvas waiting to be painted. Engineers are concerned primarily with drainage, with balancing cut and fill, and with maintaining consistent grades (See ILLUSTRATIONS 15 & 16). Although landscape architects consider these issues, they are more concerned with the relationship of the road to surrounding features. For this reason, engineers designed roads only with center line surveys and simple plans, but landscape architects demanded topographic, i.e., three-dimensional, plans of the areas through which roads would pass, so that they could be sited to take advantage of good views, outstanding trees or shrub communities, unusual rock outcrops, and other nearby features.

ILLUSTRATION 15: Standard Road Cross-Section

Early road engineers were concerned with the balancing of cut (the rock and earth removed to build a level road surface) with fill (the rock and earth needed to build up a level road surface). Importing fill, or removing cut, from a work site is a labor-intensive and expensive process; reaching a balance of cut and fill is the most economical method of road construction. Construction of the Skyline Drive made this balance more critical, since there was no easy way to bring fill to the site or to remove excess cut.

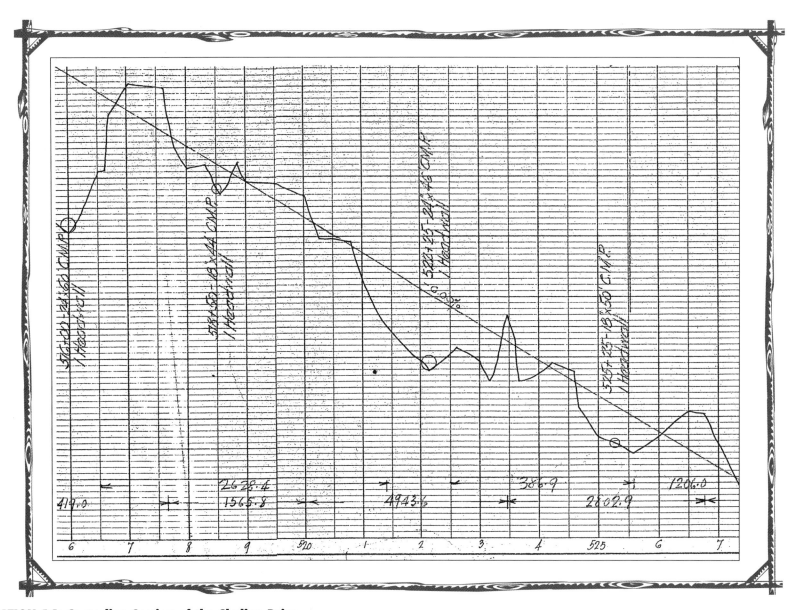

ILLUSTRATION 16: Centerline Section of the Skyline Drive

This portion of the 1931 BPR construction drawings for the Skyline Drive shows an area just north of the Marys Rock Tunnel. The jagged line indicates the original topography (the exaggerated vertical scale is typical of engineering sections) and the straight diagonal line shows the required grade for the new roadbed. The proposed 6% road gradient attempted to balance cut and fill along the length of the road as well as perpendicularly (that is, across the slope) and to be manageable for vehicles. The plan also indicates locations where headwalls needed to be installed for drainage culverts—in all cases in low areas in swales (small valleys) that needed to be filled. Headwalls and culverts were never used in cuts, since these were the high ground down from which storm water runs.

Historic Postcards

V-563:- 600 FOOT TUNNEL ON SKYLINE DRIVE IN VIRGINIA.

GHOST FOREST, BIG MEADOWS, SKYLINE DRIVE, VIRGINIA 1

Looking North from Jewell Hollow Overlook on Skyline Drive in Shenandoah National Park, Va. 16

SKYLINE DRIVE WINDING OVER TOP OF BLUE RIDGE MOUNTAINS   34

SEVEN BENDS OF THE SHENANDOAH RIVER FROM SKYLINE DRIVE   38

19587

FRANKLIN CLIFF FROM THE OVERLOOK ON SKYLINE DRIVE.   42

PHOTO U. S. DEPT. INT.

OLD RAG MOUNTAIN FROM SKYLINE DRIVE   44

TIMBER HOLLOW OVERLOOK ON SKYLINE DRIVE   45

PHOTO U.S. DEPT. INT.

KETTLE CANYON NEAR STONY MAN ON SKYLINE DRIVE   50

A View of Pinnacles Mountain, Skyline Drive, Virginia 52

Virginia Conservation Commission, Richmond, Va.

Skyline Drive Winding over top of Blue Ridge Mountains, Shenandoah National Park, Va. 58

SKYLINE DRIVE, VIRGINIA, LOOKING TOWARD STONY MAN PEAK

103

MOUNTAIN LAUREL ON THE SKYLINE DRIVE NEAR SWIFT RUN GAP, VA.

132

SKYLINE DRIVE, SHENANDOAH NATIONAL PARK, VA.

135

CROSSING OF LEE HIGHWAY AND SKYLINE DRIVE AT PANORAMA, VA.

137

TUNNEL ON SKYLINE DRIVE, SHENANDOAH NATIONAL PARK, VA.

139

SERPENTINE CURVES ON SKYLINE DRIVE, VIRGINIA

144

FRANKLIN CLIFFS (ROCK FORMATION) FROM THE OVERLOOK

556:—Highway and Tunnel on Skyline Trail, Shenandoah National Park, Va.

Sky-Line Drive, Shenandoah National Park

Valley View from Sky-Line Drive, Shenandoah National Park

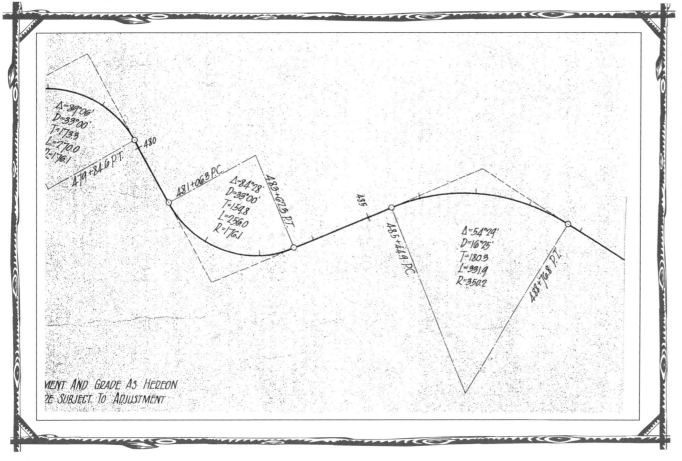

Δ=89°06'
D=33°00'
T=173.3
L=270.0
R=176.1

479+84.6 P.T.

480

481+06.3 P.C.

483+67.3 P.T.

Δ=84°28'
D=33°00'
T=159.8
L=256.0
R=176.1

485

485+44.9 P.C.

Δ=54°29'
D=16°25'
T=180.3
L=331.9
R=350.2

488+76.8 P.T.

MENT AND GRADE AS HEREON
RE SUBJECT TO ADJUSTMENT

ILLUSTRATION 17: Plan of the Centerline of the Skyline Drive

This small section of the 1931 BPR construction drawings for the Skyline Drive shows the extent of the plan views. Only the centerline and curves were shown. The subject of Clarke's critical letter, the proposed curves were simple (circular) ones; in spite of the National Park Service preference not to use curves of less than a 200' radius, some of the curves shown in the stretch of road between Marys Rock and Skyland were significantly tighter and remain difficult for motorists to this day.

In an attempt to gain the upper hand in roadway design, Roswell Ludgate, Assistant Landscape Architect under Peterson in the Eastern Office in Yorktown, wrote to William Austin on June 23, 1932, "submitting an outline of procedure . . . for our future road work in the proposed Shenandoah National Park." He stated that after "several years of experimenting, a successful method of procedure has been worked out between our San Francisco office and the western regional office of your Bureau [BPR]. This method has worked towards smooth progress and a more perfect understanding . . . . Now that the high tension of the early days [the frantic rush to survey, design, and contract the first section of the Skyline Drive] is over, this seems entirely possible." Ludgate went on to request that:

1. The Bureau engineer notify the landscape architect that he is going to flag out the preliminary survey . . . . If the engineer and landscape architect work together from the start, much time can be saved.

2. When the first transit line is run, topography is taken so that a spline line can be projected intelligently on paper in the office . . . .

6. It is very desirable that the special topography necessary for planning parking areas and other features be submitted to the landscape architect early enough so that their construction can be incorporated into the [construction] contract when advertised.

In the matter of design . . .

1. Double spiral curves will be used in place of the circular ones which have been in vogue during recent years. This tends to give an easier driving road and has a better landscape effect.

2. All earth slopes, particularly in open places shall be flattened and rounded . . . . [125]

Although beginning in the late 1920s the NPS had road standards for work on western roads incorporated in the "Special Provisions" (i.e., the NPS-specific design standards) section of BPR's road specifications, they needed modification for eastern work. The Skyline Drive project, the first major eastern park road, served as a testing ground for new design concepts and alternative ways of road building. The following summer, Peterson sent a three-page letter special delivery to Bishop, BPR Chief of Construction, outlining eleven new standards—ranging from the treatment of "trees and shrubs of value" to the "rounding of cut slopes"—that he wanted added to the "Special Provisions." [126] Clearly, the design process of the National Park Service was maturing rapidly and the landscape architects were taking greater charge of road design process.

On August 29th Chief of the Bureau of Public Roads MacDonald wrote to Demaray that the "matter of alignment is likely to be overdone by too much correspondence." He continued:

However, the road was designed with provision for spiraling all curves and compensating for grade . . . . As to the alignment of the Shenandoah National Park, the

curves are being perfected in detail and where possible compound or simple curves will be used as suggested. I have no question that the road as built will be free from any reasonable criticism as to its alignment. [127]

With the establishment of the Civilian Conservation Corps in March 1933 the National Park Service budget was increased to allow the hiring of staff to supervise CCC field projects, one of which was work on the Skyline Drive. Peterson was able to hire two landscape architects to work on Shenandoah National Park projects, Roland W. Rogers (formerly Chief Landscape Architect of the Maryland National Capital Park and Planning Commission) and Lynn M. Harriss, a young landscape graduate from the University of Iowa. Rogers served as Shenandoah National Park's Assistant Landscape Architect; [128] Harriss started as a Junior Landscape Architect and was promoted to Assistant when Rogers left in February 1935. Both men worked for the National Park Service in contrast to the many architects, landscape architects, and engineers who came to the park from 1933-1942 directly on the CCC payroll.

Harriss and Rogers immediately started to implement the new landscape design standards on the Skyline Drive. The northern extension of the Skyline Drive, still in the design process, became a proving ground for the standards Ludgate and Peterson had sent to the Bureau of Public Roads the previous summer. Harriss surveyed the entire alignment in the north district, noting elements of interest, photographing the outstanding views, and recommending locations of future parking areas and

PHOTOGRAPH 17: Lynn Harriss and Roland Rogers
Lynn Harriss (left) and Roland Rogers, NPS Landscape Architects for the Skyline Drive from 1933-1935, posed in front of the Shenandoah National Park Office (leased from Ferdinand Zerkel) in 1934.

potential sites for developments. He carefully marked these on topographic maps and sent extensive illustrated reports to Peterson for his review before final recommendations were forwarded to the Bureau of Public Roads. The landscape architects were finally initiating design instead of reacting to BPR's plans.

Spiral Curves

The design of early park roads owes more to the engineering designs developed for late 19th century railroads than to roads improved for horse-drawn wagons and carriages. A horse and rider in the late 19th century might have averaged four miles per hour on a long trip, stagecoaches with frequent changes in horses were rapid at six to seven miles/hour, and wagon trains crossing the country typically averaged fifteen miles per day. [129] Excessive speed requiring the recognition of the laws of physics had little bearing on road design until the advent of the automobile.

Trains, however, even in their earliest years in the 1830s, traveled at the unheard of speed of 20 mph. By the third quarter of the century that speed had been tripled, and traditional track design was not adequate. The physical law popularly, if incorrectly, [130] known as centrifugal force came to bear as faster and larger trains went through curves: if trains maintained their speed going through curves, they appeared to be pushed outward by centrifugal force, leading to excessive wear on the outer wheels. If trains slowed down as they approached curves, the ride was jerky and time was lost. In response to the problem, railroad designers began to use the spiral curve.

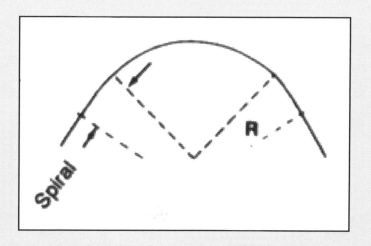

ILLUSTRATION 18: Spiral Curve

Straight roads meeting circular curves require less overall right-of-way width, although they do mandate either abruptly reduced speed limits or wider paved lanes. The insertion of spiral curves as transitions between the circular curve and the straight road sections requires wider rights-of-way, but allows for a constant speed limit and narrower paved lanes.

Used as a transition into a circular (or simple) curve, a spiral curve is less abrupt and allows the use of more constant speed. When combined with superelevation (the raising of the rails on the outside of curve to a higher grade than the inner ones), the spiral curve significantly eliminated the effects of mechanical forces on railroad travel. [131]

By the 1920s National Park Service designers were building roads specifically for the automobile, not for stagecoaches. Just as it had with trains, the spiral curve became an answer for the problems associated with automobile velocity. The curve brought with it aesthetic advantages not found with the traditional engineering approaches to road design. Because the forces tending to cause automobiles to move outward when in curves were reduced, road widths did not have to accommodate the outward thrust and resultant drift of vehicles and thus could be narrower. Aesthetically, spiral curves resulted in less abrupt transitions and provided ever-changing views—they allowed roads to conform more gently to the existing topography.

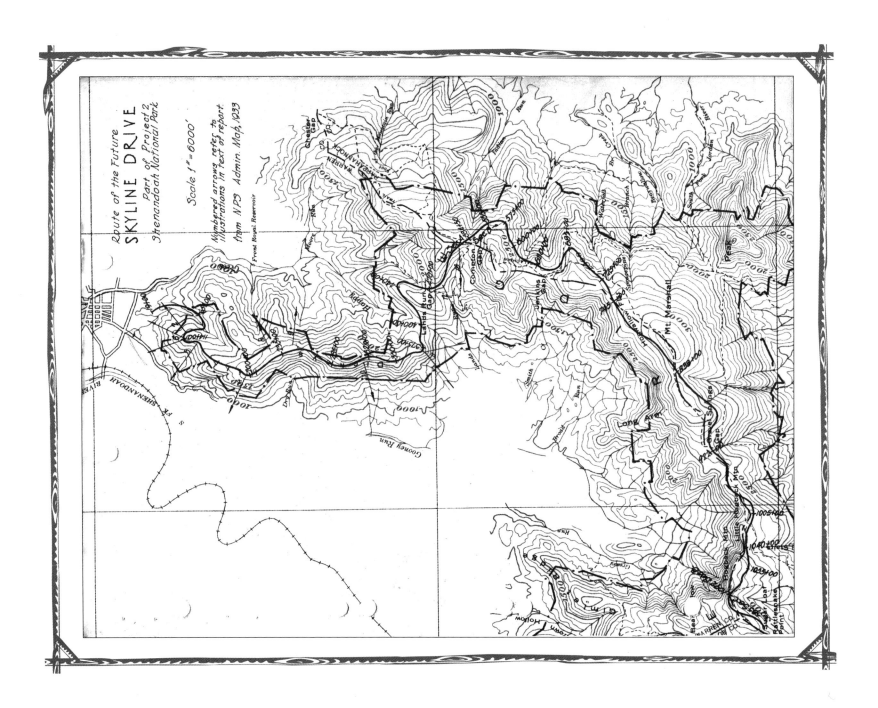

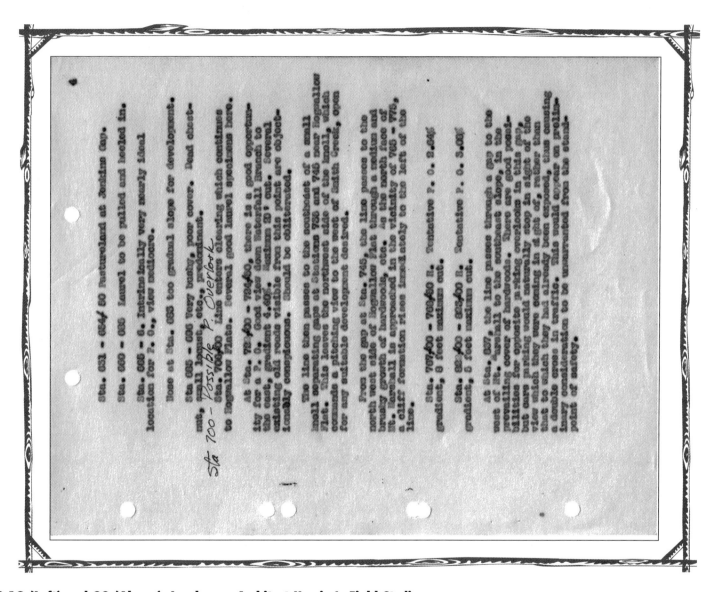

ILLUSTRATIONS 19 (Left) and 20 (Above): Landscape Architect Harriss's Field Studies

These two sheets from Harriss's "Report on Project 2A" and "Report on Project 2B" show the attention to detail paid by the NPS landscape architects in designing the alignment and special features of the Skyline Drive, once they took the driver's seat, for the north and south district portions of the roadway. Illustration 19 shows Harriss's carefully detailed topographic map with arrows showing views corresponding to photographs in the report; most photographs were locations Harriss suggested for overlooks, parking areas, or developments. Illustration 20, a sheet from Harriss's report on Section 2B of the north district, indicates the attention paid to detail by the landscape architects. Harriss noted mountain laurel to be saved before construction, good views, and locations for proposed development.

PHOTOGRAPH 18: Panoramic Planning View Near Turk Gap

Although intensively detailed planning took place on the ground, it also took place from a great distance. Park landscape architects studied the proposed alignment of the Skyline Drive from high elevation photographs to see the visual impacts not easily recognizable on the ground or from maps. This photograph in a Harriss report studied the proposed alignment of the roadway from approximately milepost 90 looking south toward Turk Gap. Photographs of proposed alignments were made for both the north and south districts of the park before final engineering surveys were completed.

Mother Nature, Politics, and The Design Process

There is a natural law that rock, earth, and gravel on a slope become stable, that is cease sliding, only when they reach the "angle of repose." Over long periods of time, all natural slopes attempt to reach this angle. The angle of repose varies from 28 degrees to 46 degrees and is dependent on the type of material on the slope, but the generally accepted standard is 34 degrees (a 1½:1 slope). The 1½:1 slope was the standard adopted by the National Park Service landscape architects in design for roads in the western parks because it was aesthetically pleasing, prevented landslides, and needed the least excavation without costly retaining walls or other structures to retain unstable slopes. Attempting to establish stable slopes consistent with the angle of repose, however, was dependent on having adequate land on which to build cut-and-fill slopes. In the western parks, the government owned all the land; in the future Shenandoah National Park, the roadway, by political necessity, had to be built on a narrow strip of land snaking across steep mountain slopes. In many locations retaining walls of one type or another had to be constructed to maintain the slopes adjacent to the new roadway.

Cut and fill was not always required; there were occasions in which it was necessary to fill without cutting adjacent slopes. Typically these involved the need to meet a consistent gradient along the length of the road, particularly when there was a wide swale running down the slope. In these instances, dry-laid embankments were laid on one or both sides of the built-up fill for the roadbed.

On occasion the use of dry-laid retaining walls was by preference, not need. Ludgate wrote to Peterson on November 10, 1931, in relation to disposal of the rock excavated from the Marys Rock Tunnel that the Bureau of Public Roads

plans to dispose of a portion of the rock from the tunnel excavation by increasing the slope of the large fill on the Panorama side from 1½ to a 1 to 1 slope. This will be accomplished by building a small wall at the toe of the present fill and hand placing the rock which comes from the tunnel. The result will be a widening of 18 feet at the tunnel entrance which will extend about two hundred feet toward Panorama. Because of the magnificent view which greets the eye on emerging from the tunnel at this point, I feel the widening here as proposed is entirely feasible. [132]

In cases where it was not possible to use either hand-laid rock embankments or toe walls because of the extreme grade of the original slopes, the road designers had to resort to the use of gabions at the road edge. Gabions, historically first used by miners and bridge builders, are large timber (today concrete) baskets which when infilled with stone allow almost vertical walls to be constructed and which distribute weight over a larger area than retaining walls. The Civilian Conservation Corps built gabion walls in several known locations along the Skyline Drive, using creosoted chestnut timbers for their construction.

Toe walls, hand-laid rock embankments, and occasional gabion walls became integral parts of the design process for the Skyline Drive, but their cost and the limitations they imposed were among the primary reasons the National Park Service later insisted upon a wider right-of-way for the Blue Ridge Parkway.

Although the toe walls and dry-laid embankments did support the roadbed of the Skyline Drive, the adjacent steep slopes necessitated by the narrow right-of-way were frequently unstable. Sheet erosion, gullies, rockslides, and road failure were common. Even when there was adequate room within the right-of-way to establish stable slopes, the contractors' mechanical equipment limited slope flattening to a vertical 10'-12' road surface, the reach of a steam shovel. [133] Reducing the gradient on higher slopes was pick-and-shovel work that would have to be accomplished by the Civilian Conservation Corps.

Harvey Benson, then Assistant Landscape Architect for CCC projects, stated his viewpoint on slope flattening in a letter to the Bureau of Public Roads:

You are entirely correct about the flattening of slopes in all three sections. The cutting back should be carried out consistently through the whole project and not confined to areas where material is required for filling or topping.

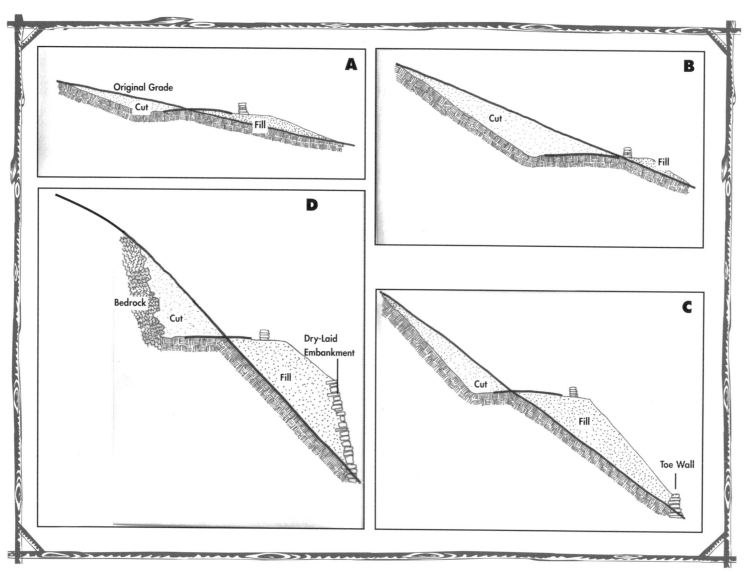

ILLUSTRATION 21: Cross-sections Showing Four Solutions to Varied Gradients

Illustrations A-D show some of the varied situations encountered in Shenandoah National Park. Where original grade slopes of 2½:1 or less were encountered (examples A & B), the paved road, grassy road shoulders, and requisite ditch and guard wall could be installed and adequate room remain on the right-of-way to construct cut and fill slopes at the angle of repose, i.e., at 1½:1. When original grade was at the angle of repose (example C), the cut and fill slopes could meet a stable grade only on the upper cut slope; the fill slope required the introduction of stone retaining wall at the base of the slope, typically at the exact edge of the 100' right-of-way. This "toe wall" supported the fill slope that often was 1:1 (45 degree). The most extreme conditions were found when the original mountain slopes were 1:1, not at all unusual. In these locations, dry-laid embankments, massive stones set into the fill slope at very steep angles as it was built up, were undertaken (example D). Typically dry-laid embankments were built in areas with underlying rock outcrops, and almost vertical rock faces were exposed on upper cut slopes.

PHOTOGRAPH 19: Hand-laid Rock Embankment

This view of the construction of a typical hand-laid rock embankment shows the difficulty of retaining slopes in very steep areas. The very narrow roadbed at the upper right portion of the view had been constructed to allow trucks to carry stone to the site to build the embankment. Note that the area behind the wall is being filled with rubble stone that is then covered with the carefully hand-laid stone whose angle is guided by the long wood forms. Once the stone construction was completed, the roadbed could be widened and the upper cut slope constructed.

69

PHOTOGRAPH 20: Browns Gap Toe Wall

This view of the Skyline Drive looking north toward milepost 82 (Browns Gap) reveals the massive toe wall on the west side of the road required because of the very steep slopes on the right-of-way. Doyles River Overlook is visible just at the top center of the photograph at the point that the road meets the horizon. This wall, like most, is not seen from the Skyline Drive today because vegetation blankets the lower slopes.

That is what an engineer would do but since we have a certain amount of check and supervision on the work, the job will not be approved until all slopes are laid back accordingly . . . . We had anticipated using a typical set of cross sections on the plans but in a conference with Mr. Peterson in Washington the other day, this has been thrown out as being too mechanical and standardized . . . [It] can only be done by viewing the situation in the field and then flattening the slopes accordingly. [134]

Peterson's demand that slope flattening not become a cliché, but be sensitive to each individual location, was summed up by Thomas J. Allen, Regional Director of Region One, NPS, in a speech to the Virginia Highway Conference in 1948:

The National Park Service slopes both cuts and fills . . . to blend artificially produced topography into existing adjacent ground forms in a manner that reflects the general appearance of the surrounding terrain. Such work requires consistently changing slope ratios, especially near the ends of cuts and fills, and adequate sloping rounding to eliminate sharp unnatural ground lines. The effect of such work certainly does improve the appearance of the Roadside . . . . and offers a surface which is well adapted to aid the natural process of revegetation. In addition to that, any stabilized and revegetated slope reduces washing and erosion. [135]

PHOTOGRAPH 21: Jeremys Gap Toe Wall

This toe wall south of Jeremys Gap shows the excellent craftsmanship of the stone masonry along the Skyline Drive. Note the well-squared stones and the tightness of the joints. Although the hand-laid rock embankments were dry-laid, most toe walls were set in mortar.

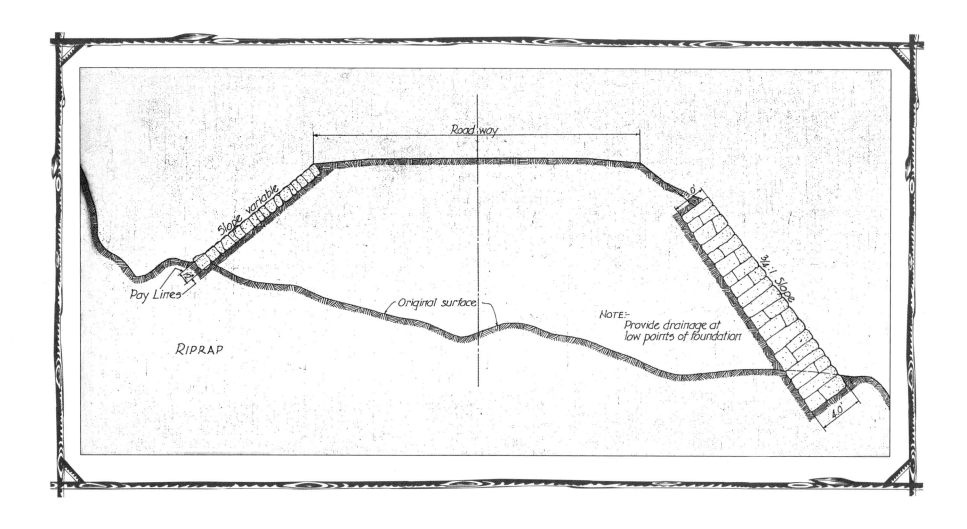

ILLUSTRATION 22: Section Showing Fill Used to Maintain Consistent Gradient

In order to meet a consistent gradient along the length of the roadbed, there were instances in which grade had to be built up significantly higher than the original. In these cases, dry-laid embankments were built on one or both sides of the fill to retain the new higher grade. The walls continued until the new raised grade met cut slopes or those not requiring structural support farther along the roadbed.

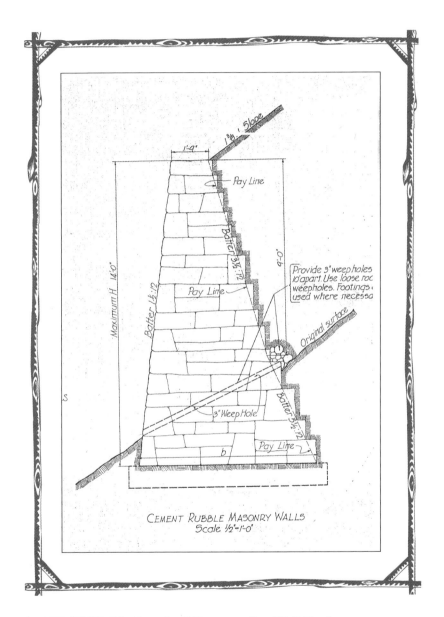

Maximum H. 14'-0"

1'-9"

Slope
1 ³⁄₈:1

Pay Line

Batter 3¹⁄₂:12

Pay Line

Provide 3" weep holes
10' apart. Use loose roc
weepholes. Footings
used where necessa

Original surface

9'-0"

3" Weep Hole

Batter 3¹⁄₂:12

b

Pay Line

CEMENT RUBBLE MASONRY WALLS
Scale ¹⁄₂"=1'-0'

ILLUSTRATION 23: Standard Masonry Toe Wall Design

This standard specification drawing for mortared masonry toe walls was included in the initial 1931 contracts for work on the central section of the Skyline Drive.

PHOTOGRAPH 22: Dry-laid Retaining Wall at Marys Rock Tunnel

Installed in 1931/32, the remarkably steep dry-laid retaining wall just north of the Marys Rock Tunnel is evidence of the artifice of the designed landscape of the Skyline Drive. Over time this slope has been softened by vegetative growth and by the slippage of the hand-laid rocks. Few visitors today would realize that it was an artificial construction.

PHOTOGRAPHS 23 (Left) & 24 (Above): Initial Gabion Installation and Covered Gabions

Photograph 23 demonstrates the initial installation of gabions along a severe slope. A terrace is cut, and upon it interleaved stacks of timbers are laid, half running into the bank, the others parallel to it. Once the timbers are placed, the interiors of the gabions are filled with boulders choked tightly with gravel.

Photograph 24 shows the filled gabions covered with soil and a stone guard wall being constructed on the finished upper surface. A portion of this log gabion wall near Milepost 13 was replaced with concrete gabions in the 1980s when the chestnut logs began to fail.

PHOTOGRAPHS 25-28: Sheet Erosion, Mudslide, Rockslide, and Roadbed Failure (Counterclockwise from upper left)

The very steep cut-and-fill slopes imposed by the original narrow right-of-way for the Skyline Drive soon led to problems. Sheet erosion leading to the formation of gullies (Photograph 25, top left) was common. Mudslides caused by the saturation of steep earth slopes (Photograph 26, lower left) were less common, but not unusual. Rockslides were frequent in the early years after the banks were first cut (Photograph 27, below) and more severe when the slides caused the complete roadbed to fail (Photograph 28, next page). These issues were not corrected until the park was established in December 1935 and sufficient land adjacent to the roadway was acquired, so that cut slopes could be laid back to more gentle grades and revegetated, work undertaken by the CCC.

PHOTOGRAPH 29: Harvey Benson Building a Model

Harvey Benson was hired by the ECW (Emergency Conservation Work) 1933 as a Jr. Landscape Architect to work on Civilian Conservation Corps projects. By late 1935 Rodgers and Harriss were gone and Benson became Shenandoah National Park's Resident Landscape Architect. He remained in the position until 1941, when he resigned for the duration of WWII. This photograph shows Benson making a model for the overpass at Swift Run Gap.

Rectifying Erosion and Blending the Banks

It has been said that the "stabilization and naturalization of the cut-and-fill scars resulting from road and highway construction was the most important work carried out by the Civilian Conservation Corps in the national parks." [136] NPS landscape architects throughout the country were focused on correcting the negative aspects of road construction:

> We should not consider that Erosion Control work has been completed in the park until every cut and fill slope along all roads . . . has been stabilized to a point where there is no more erosion either from slides, rainfall, or other natural conditions except accidental occurrences. We need not go into the many methods from which the best should be selected to apply to each project, it is sufficient to mention here that any method will result in greatly increased beauty when stabilization is actually accomplished. [137]

Few parks had to deal with as many erosion problems, however, as did Shenandoah on the Skyline Drive. Most park roads were designed with an adequate right-of-way to address slope issues as part of original design and construction. Until park establishment, the Civilian Conservation Corps spent hundreds of thousands of man-days stabilizing eroding slopes. Typically this involved building

PHOTOGRAPH 30: Erosion Control

On this badly eroded slope the Civilian Conservation Corps is constructing cribbing of large saplings, installed horizontally along the slope, held in place with stakes installed vertically up the slope face. In the center of the slope outcropping rock is left exposed. On the left of the photograph, the erosion control work has been completed and mulch is being applied to the planted surface.

cribbing, loose baskets of interwoven saplings and twigs, upon the faces of steep slopes. The cribs were then back-filled with topsoil, seeded or sodded, occasionally planted with seedlings, and mulched.

Although erosion control on the cut-and-fill slopes along the Skyline Drive was mandatory if the roadway was to continue to exist, Shenandoah's landscape architects were concerned with more than just stability. They wanted the road to blend into the adjacent slopes, seemingly a natural occurrence. Harold Fowler,

Resident Landscape Architect at Sequoia National Park, wrote of the planting program along the General's Highway there, a roadway that Charles Peterson had surveyed with William Austin years before:

> The steep cut slopes and hills form an ugly scar that has been slow to encourage plant growth. This planting project will help materially to hasten a naturalistic roadside planting . . . . The object has been to blend the new slope planting into the existing growth above the cut slopes. It is not intended that this

planting should look like a formal border mass. The object has been to blend the new slope planting into the existing growth above the cut slopes. [138]

Blending slopes took many forms along the Skyline Drive. Where slopes abutted open pastures, the CCC trenched narrow ditches and planted strips of sod lifted from areas to be developed for picnic grounds and campgrounds. In other areas the Civilian Conservation Corps enrollees laid back the banks to a gentler gradient, allowing fingers of existing trees and shrubs to remain in place, and planted masses of shrubs to extend the natural understory down the slope. In specific cases where isolated rock outcrops seemed "isolated" and artificial, the CCC installed rock talus slopes below the outcrops to make the area more naturalistic.

PHOTOGRAPH 31: Erosion Control (Above Left)

This view of cribbing installed on an almost vertical slope shows that cribbing, topsoil, and planting were undertaken only on the areas between rock outcrops or bare rock faces. Note the heavy matting of mulch applied over the cribbing, topsoil, and seed.

PHOTOGRAPH 32: Sod Strip Installation (Left)

On a slope below an open field, the CCC installed strips of grass sod, either lifted from areas to be developed or purchased from nurseries, to blend the slope into the adjacent vegetation.

PHOTOGRAPH 33: Bank Blending

The Civilian Conservation Corps laid back the slopes to a more gentle gradient, when possible, leaving fingers of existing trees and shrubs to extend into the new slopes, and planted vegetation that closely resembled the adjacent plant material.

PHOTOGRAPH 34: Installing a Talus Slope

Shenandoah's landscape architects were concerned with slopes that appeared artificial. Civilian Conservation Corps enrollees in this photograph are installing boulders and rocks on a slope below a rock outcrop to make it appear more like a "natural" rock talus slope.

Through Solid Rock

The Marys Rock Tunnel excites few of
Shenandoah National Park's visitors today,
although some do stop to take photographs
near the south portal. People today are used to far
longer modern tunnels, but in 1931 visitors were
thrilled by the engineering feat, and the tunnel on the
Skyline Drive was a much-admired curiosity. Because
of its novelty, Marys Rock Tunnel became an iconic
image used on almost all early park souvenirs.

By the middle of the 19th century railroad and
canal companies engineered, designed, and built
tunnels—they had no choice but to go through high
ground they could not go around. Highway
engineers and landscape architects learned from
railroad technology. The single-lane 900' long Nada
Tunnel in Red River Gorge in Kentucky was
completed in 1911. The Columbia River Highway
near Portland, Oregon, completed in 1921, included
three tunnels. A few cities built tunnels under
adjacent rivers: Chicago's Washington Street Tunnel,
completed in 1869, was one of the earliest, but it was
not until the third decade of the 20th century that
urban tunnels such as New York's Holland Tunnel
(1927) became more common.

The early Hoover-era Great Depression public
works funding, the labor force of the Civilian
Conservation Corps, and the funding from FDR's
Public Works Administration led to a binge of
National Park Service tunnel construction during the
1930s. Because most national parks were in rugged
terrain not suitable for road building, tunnels
provided an alternate for the massive scars that could
have been created had traditional road techniques
been used. The 5,613' long Zion-Mount Carmel
Tunnel in Zion National Park was dedicated in 1930,
before the Roosevelt programs. Four tunnels,
however, were constructed in Yosemite National Park
during the Roosevelt years, with the first dedicated
in 1933, as was Glacier National Park's Going-to-the-
Sun Highway Tunnel. In the late 1930s three tunnels
were completed in Great Smoky Mountains National
Park, and 26 tunnels on the Blue Ridge Parkway
were constructed from 1935-1966.

Yet it was not until the Pennsylvania Turnpike
was completed in 1940 that tunnels were accepted as
a routine part of highway construction in the eastern
states. Built partially on a former railroad right-of-
way, the "tunnel turnpike" incorporated six recycled
rail tunnels and one new one.

The decision to build the tunnel at Marys Rock
was made by the Bureau of Public Roads with the
concurrence of the National Park Service. The
agencies were truly between a very large rock and a
steep place. As seen in Illustration 24, the summit of
Marys Rock is almost 200' above the floor of the
tunnel, and the roadway on either side was designed
to meet the contours of the mountains and to meet
Panorama at the crest of the Blue Ridge. If the
roadway hadn't gone through the mountain, the
rock ridge would have had to be cut back at least a
thousand feet to the west, creating a 500' high slope
at a 1:1 (45 degree) angle. Clearly such an
excavation would have been tremendously
expensive, would have created a massive quantity of
waste material, and would have resulted in an
unsightly scar, subject to landslides. Tunneling was
the only logical choice.

After first reviewing the drawings, Assistant
Landscape Architect Peterson wrote to BPR's
Bishop questioning how the tunnel entrance portals
would be treated:

> If the tunnel idea is to be carried out do you think that
> the rock will break nicely at the portal or will it be
> necessary to build up a new facing? You probably
> remember that both conditions existed at the Zion-Mt.
> Carmel tunnels [where one portal had to be faced with
> stone and the other was left unfaced]. [139]

Peterson and Bishop deferred a decision on an
artificial entrance until construction determined how
the rock in the ridge split.

The public was enthralled with the project. *The
Madison Eagle* reported in November 1931:

> An average of 1,000 pounds of dynamite is being used
> daily . . . . Five hundred pounds . . . is loaded into 40
> holes and set off by electricity twice in 24 hours. These
> holes are drilled to a depth of 12 feet, three or four feet
> apart, over the face wall at the end of the tunnel, the
> object being to carry the tunnel back at its full height
> and width all the time. Every day 15 or more feet of
> solid rock are eaten away by the blasts . . . . Work is
> progressing steadily and satisfactorily and the tunnel

PHOTOGRAPH 35: Rockslide at Marys Rock

The avoidance of rockslides down the cut slope of Marys Rock was one of the primary reasons the tunnel was built. However, just south of the tunnel where the ridge is less steep but still significant, slides have been frequent. This slide, in June 1941, closed both lanes of the Skyline Drive.

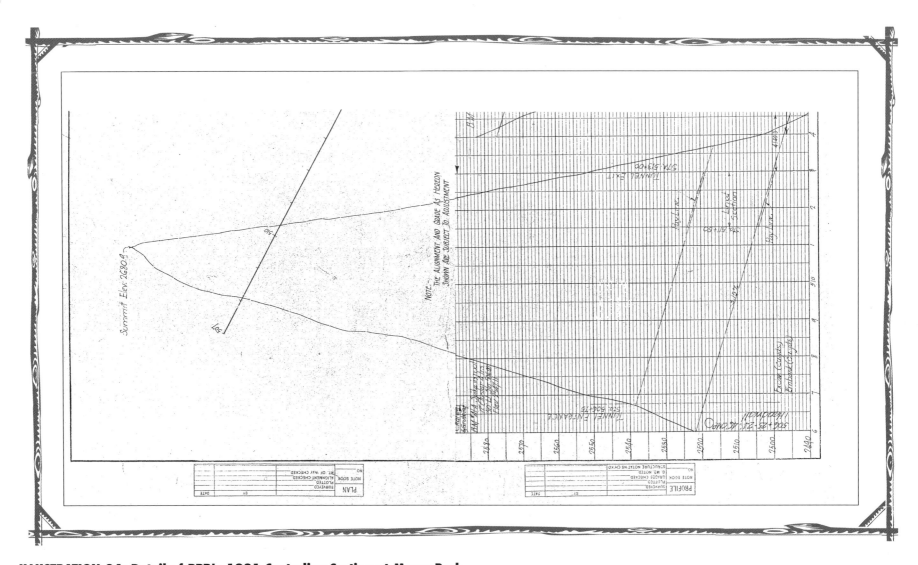

ILLUSTRATION 24: Detail of BPR's 1931 Centerline Section at Marys Rock

Detail from the "Plans for Proposed Project No. 1 Section Blue Ridge Skyline Drive," signed by the NPS and the BPR, June 9, 1931, and used for construction bids. [140] The engineering centerline cross-section has a horizontal scale in units of 100' and a typical engineer's vertical scale in units of 10', thereby greatly exaggerating the vertical proportions. Note, however, how Marys Rock (summit marked "2,680.9") goes well off the standard engineering grid paper. The proposed tunnel is shown as twin diagonal lines near the bottom of the sheet. The tunnel starts at an elevation of 2,494' above sea level at the south portal and rises to 2,522' at the north portal, a gentle 3.15% grade change.

should be driven through by some time in January . . . . After the blast goes off with a mighty roar it requires two to three hours to clear away the loose boulders and stone and to roll them over the side of the dizzy fill at the mouth of the tunnel. Three 8-hour shifts of about 15 men each are on duty . . . the machinery never being idle except on Sunday . . . .The labor on the job is paid from 20 to 35 cents an hour. [141]

In January 1932 the blasting broke through the north portal of the tunnel; almost 11,000 cubic yards of granite had been removed. Within a week traffic was streaming through, although the roadway was not officially open. [142]

Peterson wrote to Bishop on January 29, 1932:

I have just visited the Shenandoah Park project with Mr. Austin [BPR] and Mr. Ludgate [Asst. Landscape Architect, NPS, Eastern Division]. On this occasion we inspected the Mary's Rock tunnel, which is now at least roughly completed. We are of the opinion that since the rock broke so nicely around the natural portal, that it would not be wise to build any architectural masonry portals on either end . . . .

It is, however, recommended, and I know you will agree, that some measures be taken to retain the sliding . . . slope above the north portal. The best way to do this, we feel, is to anchor weather rock from the surrounding slopes into the barren patch above the tunnel entrance in a naturalistic way with large cavities holding earth in which a planting of native shrubs and trees can be made. The most desirable effect is a

perfectly natural one of imitating the surrounding slopes. A project of this sort was carried out in one of the Rockefeller carriage roads on the side of Jordan Pond in Acadia National Park. This tunnel work, however, would not be nearly so extensive or costly. It is, however, rather exacting type of work and it will be necessary for Mr. Ludgate, as Landscape Architect, to be continuously on hand during its progress. [143]

Bishop responded to Peterson on February 1st that he was in complete agreement about the tunnel portals. [144] But Peterson's plan to anchor boulders in a naturalistic manner to stop rockslides adjacent to

PHOTOGRAPH 36: North End of Marys Rock

Although the roadbed from Panorama to the north end of the proposed Marys Rock Tunnel had been temporarily graded by late Autumn 1931, the contractors would not break through from the south until January. Note the highly unstable rock slopes above what would become the tunnel portal. These slopes later required the construction of terraced retaining walls.

PHOTOGRAPH 37: South Portal of the Tunnel, October 1933

Although the Skyline Drive was closed to automobiles because the roadbed had still not been paved and guardwalls, guardrails, and overlooks not yet completed, visitors walked from Panorama to view the new tunnel. The tunnel had not yet been widened to provide room for a gutter on the west (left) side and a sidewalk on the east. Note the numerous large boulders on the slopes above the portal.

the north portal, if it ever was executed, did not work. By July 1934 the north portal of the tunnel was again being discussed because rockslides were impacting the roadway:

> Dear Mr. Peterson:
>
> We looked over the north portal of the Mary's Rock Tunnel, having at hand the topo[graphic map] taken by the Bureau [of Public Roads] and a model of the same scale which I had made in the office . . . . It was finally agreed that Mr. Austin would strip the overburden [all loose rock and soil above bedrock] back as far as he considered feasible, construct protecting cribbing [to protect the road below from rockslides], and obtain topography of this exposed [rock] ledge, on the basis of which we could collaborate the definite location of the wall. This, together with my version of the stonework would appear on a sheet to be submitted to you for recommendation and on to the Bureau for design.
>
> Very Truly Yours,
> Lynn M. Harriss
> Jr. Landscape Architect
> Shenandoah National Park [145]

Harriss and Austin reached agreement in the field, and the two stone retaining walls still in place on the north portal were installed.

But the problems with the tunnel were not over. The original design was too narrow for public use. Harvey Benson, Assistant Landscape Architect, wrote Peterson in December 1934 that the tunnel was "being widened [by four feet] to a width of twenty-seven feet . . . [to accommodate] a twenty-two foot roadway, a three foot pedestrian walk and built-in curb on the east side and a two foot curb and ditch on the west side [to deal with the water dripping into the tunnel from springs above]." [146] Benson also discussed, at length, plans to provide electric lighting for the interior of the tunnel, eventually abandoned since newer cars came equipped with better electric headlights. [147]

One final problem with the tunnel, and one that still remains to a lesser extent, was the constant seeping from springs uncovered during excavation. Although subsequent lining of the tunnel has partially corrected the problem, the north portal retains its spectacular icicles every winter.

PHOTOGRAPHS 38-40: Constructing the North Portal Walls

(Clockwise From Left)
The construction of the rock retaining walls above the north portal of the Marys Rock Tunnel began in the fall of 1935. It required cutting two terraces down to bedrock in the rocky slope above the entrance and the construction of massive stone "steps" beside the portal to stabilize the slope and to allow access to the terraces above (Photograph 38). Using a winch and bucket, huge roughly-faced stones were set as a hand-laid rock retaining wall on the lower (Photograph 39) and then the upper terrace (Photograph 40).

**PHOTOGRAPH 41:
Interior of Marys Rock
Tunnel in Winter**

This early interior view of the
tunnel indicates the winter
conditions before the concrete
lining was installed in 1958-
1959. Today, the north portal still
exhibits icicles that, on occasion,
can reach ten feet in length.

Overlooks and Parking Areas

October 26, 1932

Dear Mr. Peterson:

Associate Director Cammerer, Mr. Bishop, Mr. Taylor and Mr. Austin [and the author, Demaray] were on the road and observed conditions. We also asked those using the road to give their comments . . . . The principal suggestions were for more parking areas at overlooks, cutting to provide better views and the early construction of a guard rail. [148]

The brief advance opening of the Skyline Drive in Autumn 1932 gave the landscape architects the opportunity to study the issues that would have to be faced when the roadway opened permanently. It has been estimated that 40% of the landscape along the road was open to some extent in 1935, providing many spectacular views of the Piedmont and the Shenandoah Valley. The first visitors just pulled off and parked anywhere the view appeared interesting, making erosion control and revegetation of the raw construction slopes and shoulders difficult. In the rush to build the roadway, the Panorama to Swift Run Gap section of the Skyline Drive had been built without consideration of overlooks and parking areas; these would have to be designed after the fact and based on established visitor use patterns. For the remainder of the road, views and vistas—both existing and able to be created—were incorporated into the analysis and design before construction.

A good case in point is Jewell Hollow Overlook. Photograph 13 (page 42), taken during the preview period in 1932, demonstrates that the first park visitors wanted to experience the view into Jewell Hollow. Peterson first suggested to Assistant Landscape Architect Rogers that a parking area be built north of the vista. After having carefully studied the area, Rogers wrote to Peterson on August 14, 1933, enclosing a preliminary plan:

As you will very likely notice the area for parking has been placed to the South-West of the view point rather than to the North-East as you suggested. This was done for the following reasons:

(1) The woods enclosing the north-east are "faced down" by a belt of young and bushy native pines which are very attractive and should be preserved if possible;

(2) The area defined by these pines is comparatively small and of such a shape that it does not lend itself well to the development of a parking space;

(3) The ground in said area slopes to the south-west at approximately a twelve degree slope which would necessitate terracing for each row of cars thus complicating the entrance and exit roads;

(4) It was the concensus [sic] of opinion here that the most logical location for parking in this place was just after the viewpoint was reached rather than before, and as about three-quarters of the traffic to stop there would be south-bound, this would indicate the location selected. [149]

After the inevitable back and forth between Peterson and Rogers, the final design incorporating most of the concepts first advocated by Rogers was forwarded to the Director for approval in October. This required the construction of a massive dry-laid retaining wall to support the elevated grade of the parking area and the mortared stone (ashlar) guardwall along the edge. Additionally, the cut slope to the south required construction of a dry-laid retaining wall into which a drinking fountain was later constructed.

Rogers' final comment to Peterson in reference to the Jewell Hollow Overlook, however, raises a very important point concerning overlook design—parking areas and overlooks were, to some extent, being designed to influence and regulate visitor behavior:

Unless some scheme like the one presented can be worked out . . . I would recommend that the road [i.e. the Skyline Drive] be pulled down hill [i.e. to the east] from its present location thus lessening the degree or curve and eliminating the view from the road [of Jewell Hollow] at this point. There would then be no necessity for any parking. [150]

In January 1934 Lynn Harriss sent Peterson a proposed design for the Rattlesnake Point Overlook and a prototypical design for parking areas with vistas to the Shenandoah Valley (ILLUSTRATIONS 25 and 26). Both illustrate this early belief in regulation. Harriss strongly felt that the parking areas should have one-way circulation and that northbound traffic should be separated from

PHOTOGRAPH 42: Jewell Hollow Overlook

This view of Jewell Hollow Overlook parking area (ca. 1935) indicates how crowded the initially-constructed sections of the Skyline Drive first were. The vegetation in the wooded area to the upper left is today more sparse, the massive rock outcroppings more visible. The field across the Drive (upper right) is shown filled with cars in Photograph 13 (page 42).

southbound. This concept was spatially executed at Jewell Hollow Overlook in the sense that the northbound traveler would have no reason to stop there because the vista of the Hollow would not be seen until the parking area had been passed. But Harriss proposed taking this one step further and designing overlooks that were laid out specifically for the direction the driver was going on the Skyline Drive. The problem with his "Suggested Scheme . . ." was that it placed the visitor directly adjacent to, and above, the Skyline Drive, attempting to view a distant scene while overlooking the roofs of passing cars in the foreground. His "Rattlesnake Point" parking overlook design was overkill; it would have required massive grading and accomplished little in the way of visitor safety or control. Both designs were rejected.

By August 1934, after a series of rather heated letters among Lassiter, Peterson, Harriss, and the NPS Director concerning a proposed overlook at Milam Gap, Jr. Landscape Architect Harriss wrote for Roland Rogers the desired policy on overlook and parking area placement, a departure from his previous designs:

> Our policy on the alignment of the Drive and the
> selection of overlook sites has been . . . [that]
> rather than bending the road to suit the views
> and placing overlooks at the best view points
> along this route, we have considered the views
> more in the preliminary routing of the road than
> in the final design . . . . This has been adhered
> to, not only for the obvious benefits to the
> alignment, . . . but also from the desire to locate

at least some of the overlooks separated from the Drive by enough distance to reduce somewhat the noise and confusion of traffic which has a tendency to disturb the effect of a quiet pastoral view such as this. [151]

This became the premise that guided future overlook design. Where separation and solitude were not possible, the landscape architects attempted to provide a vegetated island that separated the overlook from the Skyline Drive.

One of the greatest issues facing the landscape architects was capacity. Early visitation to the Skyline Drive had been overwhelming as people flocked to see the new roadway. Without considering if these numbers would be sustained over time, the park designers felt they had to build to meet this demand. Parking lots and overlooks were not only designed to meet the early crowds, they were designed to be expandable in the future.

> I am inclosing herewith the pencil tracing of the
> Franklin Cliffs Parking Overlook. Mr. Peterson feels
> that whereas the design is intrinsically good, it does not
> go far enough to the south . . . . He also feels that the
> promenade to the north lacks some reason for existence
> and something was said about moving the comfort
> station to the end of this walk so as to do two things:
> first, to give a use to the walk, and, second to remove
> the present obstacle to future expansion to the south. [152]

As the design of the Skyline Drive progressed and it became apparent that the initial surge of visitation

would lessen, the size of parking areas and overlooks decreased. The initial over-design of the parking areas and overlooks ceased as it became more apparent that the novelty of the unique mountain roadway slipped into being a byway into and through a national park.

In spite of the landscape architects' careful efforts to frame significant views, politics, always present in early Shenandoah National Park decisions, came to bear on design decisions. In January 1935 representatives of the Front Royal Chamber of Commerce, Lions Club, Rotary Club, Retail Merchants Association, and the Town Council wrote to Lassiter requesting that " a parking over-look . . . be constructed on the Sky Line Drive about two miles from Front Royal . . . ." They submitted these reasons for the request:

> (1) There is at present no parking over-look from
> which the Town of Front Royal is visible . . . .

> (2) Such location will call the attention of tourists to
> the Town and we may thereby profit locally from the
> tourist trade

> (3) We also consider this to be worthwhile because of
> added beauty and interest to that portion of the Drive
> particularly at night or in the late evening after the
> Town is illuminated.

Lassiter wrote a note to Benson on the letter: "Give me something on this." Benson did, and the Shenandoah Valley Overlook was constructed in response to the request. [153]

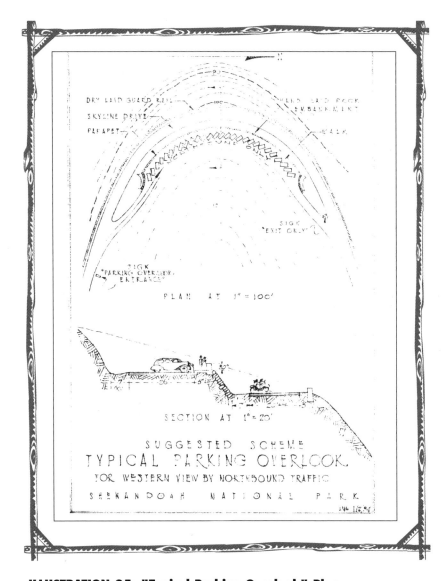

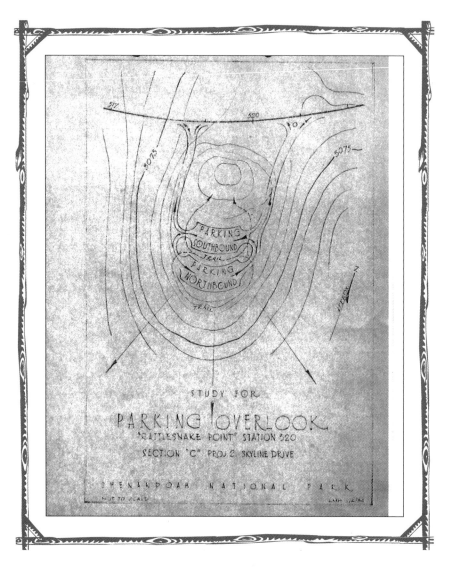

ILLUSTRATION 25: "Typical Parking Overlook" Plan

Landscape Architect Harriss developed this "Suggested Scheme" for a prototypical parking overlook for Shenandoah Valley vistas in January 1934. The basis for his concept was that only northbound traffic on the Skyline Drive would have access to this area. Unfortunately, the overlook would have placed the visitors directly adjacent to and above the through traffic, hardly a desirable situation and a concept that was not accepted. [154]

ILLUSTRATION 26: Rattlesnake Point Overlook Design

Harriss's preliminary design for this overlook indicates his desire to control the visitor flow by separating parking for northbound and southbound traffic on the Skyline Drive. Although, perhaps, based on early visitor-use patterns, the Harriss plans would have required massive amounts of excavation, cut and fill, to create results accomplished ultimately with less intrusive design by not segregating overlooks based on the direction of traffic flow.

92

After almost eight decades the overlooks along Skyline Drive are seen as an integral part of the roadway. The vistas, traffic patterns, and visitation have changed. As vegetation has matured and returned, the views no longer encourage visitors to stop at the overlooks; rather overlooks encourage travelers to stop for the views. The overlooks remain, however, a major part of the experience of the Skyline Drive.

Guardwalls and Guiderails

On June 21, 1931, Charles Peterson wrote to the Director of the National Park Service:

At the time I signed the Title Sheet for the new Shenandoah road job . . . it was my understanding that there was no guard rail to be built at this time . . . . I did not see a copy of the plans until June 28, and I note that on the last page a rustic wood guard rail is shown.

I have been favoring all along a continuous stone masonry job for this guard rail, and this is indicated in my letter of May 4ᵗʰ to Mr. Bishop . . . and I recommend that no guard rail be built on this job . . . unless it can be arranged to construct the masonry rails . . . . The finest piece of guard rail I remember having seen is the masonry rail built between Nisqually Glacier and Paradise Inn in Mount Ranier [sic] Park. Since the cleavage of the stone in Shenandoah Park is well adapted to this design, I recommend that it be used. [155]

Bishop wrote to NPS Senior Assistant Director Demaray in response to Peterson's letter and questioned "the advisability of expending the funds for masonry guard rail at this time. We purposely provided for sufficient rustic [wood] guard rail to protect the public . . . [but] I am inclined to believe we should surface [i.e., pave] this project before we attempt the refinements of a masonry guard rail." Bishop also noted that the park had a great quantity of dead chestnut trees and "that a guard rail of this type could be built for the minimum price . . . the total cost of a guard rail . . . covering 42 miles is only $3,540.00. [156] Director Albright became involved in the discussion, noting:

I kind of like the dead chestnut idea. We have got to get rid of a lot of the dead trees some time. The President [Hoover] mentioned this when we were riding. [157]

Peterson was a bulldog and never easily gave up an argument. He wrote back suggesting a guardrail using spaced boulders, which could later be crushed and used as road material. Bishop responded that this would not be cost effective. Demaray settled the issue in time-honored bureaucratic style, by postponement:

There is no one who can foretell when the Shenandoah National Park will become actually established . . . . Until this happens, we cannot count on getting any more money for the Shenandoah Road project . . . . It, therefore, would appear that either chestnut guard rails or no guard rails will be provided. As the chestnut guard rails will not be constructed until near the end of the contract, this question can be settled by the Director this fall. [158]

Temporary boulders were placed along precipitous edges as were logs, but a permanent solution was not attempted. Fourteen months later the issue lingered. Chief of BPR MacDonald wrote to Albright:

Of course you are aware of the fact that no guard rail has been erected on this portion of the project [Skyland to Panorama]. The Bureau is now . . . . preparing designs for the type to be used. We hope to submit to you in the very near future a detailed estimate so that contracts may be let for the early construction of the necessary guard rail for the entire project. [159]

In April 1933 Franklin Delano Roosevelt came to visit Rapidan Camp with Secretary of the Interior Harold Ickes, NPS Director Albright, William Carson, and several others on Roosevelt's staff. At Carson's urging the group toured the Skyline Drive on their way back to Washington, D.C. Albright later recounted the drive with the President:

When he [FDR] got to the car he put me in the jump seat; he put three in the back . . . [including] Henry Morgenthau [Secretary of the Treasury] . . . . We came up . . . and got on the Skyline . . . . He [FDR] couldn't say enough in favor of the alignment . . . . from the back seat Morgenthau kept criticizing Hoover for the expensive parapets [guard walls], because these stone parapets were being built. Two or three times he criticized Hoover extravagance . . . . just before we got to the tunnel . . . . Morgenthau made a complaint again about the parapets and the President turned around and said, "Aw, shut up, Henry . . . . Nobody gets more scared than you do. If it wasn't for that wall, you'd be out walking." [160]

Construction of walls continued in April 1933. However, they would remain a matter of contention throughout the construction of the road: between the BPR and NPS because of differing standards for judging the end product, and between Peterson and the park landscape architects and Superintendent over the aesthetics of the issue.

There were two basic types of stone guardwalls proposed for, and eventually used, on the Skyline Drive. The typical walls in the central section (the type of which Henry Morgenthau had complained) were ashlar masonry, composed of small stones laid in courses, set in mortar, and covered with large capstones. These walls had vertical faces on both sides. The second type, dry-laid walls, were built without mortar from much larger stones, several feet long, many the full height of the wall (and in some cases higher than the average). However, because they are not held together with mortar, dry-laid walls are battered (sloped) on the exterior face to resist the efforts of gravity to pull them over. Ashlar masonry walls required expert masons; dry-laid walls could be constructed with day labor or by the Civilian Conservation Corps, since their primary construction challenge was moving and aligning the large stones, not trimming and fitting them into a continuous wall.

But the NPS landscape architects were concerned with the dry-laid walls' alignment and the need for a batter. Creating a proper batter required the use of wooden guide frames along the length of the proposed wall to guide the non-expert laborers. The frames had to be set by someone with experience.

ILLUSTRATION 27: Standard Dry-laid Wall Drawing

This drawing was used for the construction of dry-laid guardwalls in both the north and south district sections of the Skyline Drive. Note that the 18" high wall was composed of large stones set vertically adjacent to the Skyline Drive, but battered, i.e., wider at the bottom of the wall than at the top, on the back (fill slope) side. The batter, which counteracts gravity, is the time-honored way of building dry-laid walls. [161]

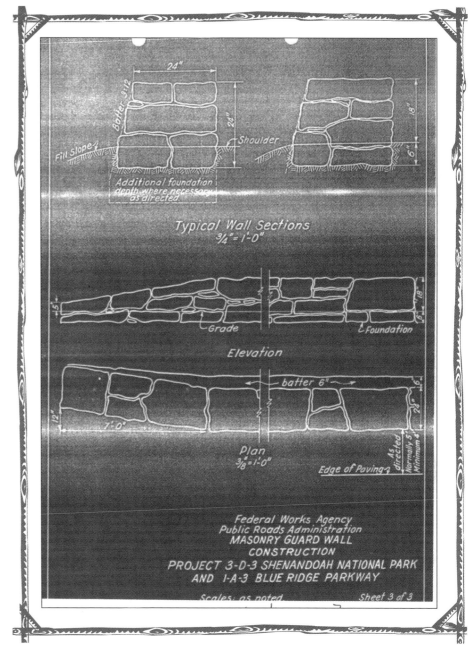

That job fell to Jr. Landscape Architect Lynn Harriss. In September 1933 Harriss sent four letters to Peterson complaining about the poor quality of the work being produced by day laborers on the dry-laid walls, his demanding workload in having to site the wooden frames, his need for a vehicle of his own, his belief that ashlar walls would produce a better landscape effect, and suggesting that a full-time supervisor was needed for landscape construction supervision. By the end of September BPR's William Austin had had his fill and testily wrote to Harriss's boss Roland Rogers with copies to Peterson, BPR Chief of Construction Bishop, and Shenandoah National Park Engineer-in-Charge Lassiter:

> This acknowledges Mr. Harriss's letter of September 26 relative to the alignment of stone guard rail on the Skyline Drive. Since the evident intent of his letter is to go on record with something, a reply with like intent is thought in order.
>
> We all know the wall is not perfect from a standpoint of alignment and according to Mr. Peterson, rightly so I think, he did not expect nor did he wish to attain perfection in the walls.
>
> It boils down to this—If an ashler [sic] effect on perfect alignment is to be attained, trained masons at an hourly rate of from $1.35 to $1.50 (instead of the 39 cents per hour wage we are paying) must be imported . . . .
>
> It is absolutely ridiculous to say that a better job, either in the quantity of work or the alignment, can be had without an appreciable increase in cost, both in the

PHOTOGRAPH 43: Wall Frames

Building dry-laid walls in the correct location to the roadway and with the correct batter required the NPS landscape architect to place wooden frames on-site for the CCC or day labor workers to use as guides. More qualified stone masons would not have needed these to construct the more expensive rubble masonry ashlar walls used in some parts of the original section of the Skyline Drive.

work and in the engineering. It is equally as ridiculous to state that the injection of a landscape foreman into the organization would improve the quality of the work without increasing costs . . . . We had might as well face the issue. If Mr. Harriss is not satisfied with the quality of the work or the alignment, the proper course of procedure is to take up with Mr. Peterson the question of securing additional funds to take care of the increased costs entailed in order to turn out work that will meet with the approval of Mr. Harriss. [163]

Rogers sent back a response to Austin that undercut Harriss and at the same time defended him. Although stating that "we do not recommend by any means that there be a change made in the construction methods or that ashlar effect is desirable . . . . We do believe that an improvement is possible in the alignment without any increase in cost . . . ." [164] Henceforth guardwalls would be of the dry-laid, unmortared type.

Although internal bureaucratic dissension appeared to have been resolved by late 1933, public reaction to the stone walls in general was not–many visitors did not like them. Peterson was required to write to a representative of the Louisville (Kentucky) Automobile Club in August 1935 after a letter of complaint to the NPS Director about them:

> We agree with you that the present effect of the stone walls tends to be monotonous. However, when the work on the shoulders is completed and natural growth comes up, the lines of the walls will be softened, and more or less inconspicuous. If you look at stone walls

along roadsides in old farming communities, you will understand what nature will do. [165]

It was not only visitors who found the stone walls monotonous. Shenandoah National Park Associate Landscape Architect Harvey Benson wrote to Peterson in relation to the Big Meadows and Milam Gap areas that " in order to relieve the monotony of the stone type of construction and to have the guard barrier in keeping with the surroundings, it is recommended that the standard log rail as shown on the Bureau [of Public Roads] plans be adopted through this section . . . . Mr. Lassiter is in accord with the log rail idea, although he feels that it should extend to Swift Run Gap." [166] Within a month Engineer in Charge (and soon to become Superintendent) Lassiter wrote to the Director:

> The work the Bureau of Public Roads has done so far [on the guardwalls] has caused many comments, both favorable and otherwise. One of the most frequent criticisms has reference to the fact that the wall cuts off too much of the view. This is especially so as one rounds the nose of some promontory . . . where the top of the wall is about level with the eyes of the visitors traversing the Drive. The wall cuts from view what would be otherwise a fine panorama of some precipitous valley, leaving the tops of distant ridges to be seen.

> An open type [wood] guard–similar to the type approved for the Shenandoah-Smokies Parkway [sic-the Blue Ridge Parkway]–would permit these views to be appreciated, and at the same time afford ample safety and protection to the visitor. [167]

Although Peterson continued to resist the use of wood guardrail, a compromise was reached. Wood rail would be used in more open areas and stone wall in forested sections, those with rock outcrops, or those with no view. By this standard Benson wrote to Chief Architect Vint in January 1936 stating that the "stone guardwall [will] be used along the Drive in the north section with the exception of the areas from Beahm Gap to Elkwallow Gap (3 miles) and from Hogwallow Flats to Jenkins Gap (2 miles). The same rationale was used in the placement of guard barriers in the South District. All in all, not counting the lowest section of today's Skyline Drive, originally part of the Blue Ridge Parkway, over eleven miles of wood guardrail were constructed by the Civilian Conservation Corps along the Skyline Drive.

By the summer of 1936 during construction of the guardwall at Fishers Gap, the general specification for dry-laid masonry walls had been modified to include the use of "extra large stones," often up to 5' in length, as a safety feature. In 1941 Benson requested that these stones be reduced in length because the contractor was complaining that they were expensive and required special machinery to manipulate. BPR discussed the issue:

> We have had an auto jump the wall but no auto has ever knocked the wall down, or gone through it, not even a truck, although a number have hit them at good speeds. The large stones may be what stop them; at least no wholesale destruction such as the 90 feet of wall leveled by a C.C.C. truck several years ago on

the curve just south of Crescent Rock Overlook . . . has ever occurred since we started using the extra large stones....

Twenty percent of the wall face [is] devoted to "extra large stones" . . . at a wall length of 2 times their wall heights [approximately 3'], as requested by Mr. Benson, every 16 ²/₃ feet, giving a space of wall between the end of the large stones of about 12 feet. Assuming this to be correct I think the large stones will stop anything in reason from going through and down the bank. [168]

BPR accepted Benson's proposal and some of the last stone walls built on the Skyline Drive used these reduced stones. The southernmost walls on the roadway were not constructed until after World War II. During the war years, new policies were implemented that forbade quarry operations within the national parks. After that, stone for the walls and curbs had to be imported from outside the park. Most of the new stone was limestone from the Shenandoah Valley, a clear break from the original landscape architects' design intent that the walls appear to be an organic part of the landscape in which they were sited, blending with the adjacent and surrounding metamorphic rock. The limestone walls speak to their time, and to the long and difficult process the construction of the Skyline Drive represents.

PHOTOGRAPH 44: Wood Guardrail

The Civilian Conservation Corps built miles of wood guardrail along the length of the Skyline Drive. Although consistently opposed by landscape architect Peterson, park staff insisted on over eleven miles of wood rails in open areas both to relieve the "monotony" of the stone walls and to allow visitors to have an unimpeded view of nearby valleys.

P719C

PHOTOGRAPH 45: Wood Guardrail Termination

The tops of the support posts were cut into inverted "Vs" and the bottoms of the rails V-notched to seat upon the posts. The ends of the guard rail sections sloped down almost to meet the ground, a more organic, natural effect than an abrupt stop.

There are over 38 miles of stone guardwalls on the Skyline Drive today (204,181 linear feet). They reflect the changes in aesthetic design standards, safety considerations, changing financial resources, and the availability of materials during the almost two decades during which the roadway was being constructed. They also reveal modern concerns for the safety standards necessary for larger vehicles traveling at higher speeds. But the walls remain emblematic of the Skyline Drive and the geologic base into which it was carved.

Stone Gutters

The original design and specifications for the construction of the Skyline Drive included only the customary earth ditches adjacent to the uphill side of the roadway to catch the overland flow of rainfall. By 1936 the ditches serving long steep stretches of the roadway in areas with adjacent springs, or those downhill from swales and mountain hollows collecting water from large areas, were deeply eroded and threatening to undermine the Skyline Drive. Harvey Benson, Resident Landscape Architect, created a design to line the earth ditches in vulnerable locations with cut stone. Benson sent his design to William Austin, Chief of Construction at BPR.

Austin wrote back to Benson on September 18, 1936, enclosing BPR revisions of the original sketch and specifications for the work. Austin said that the

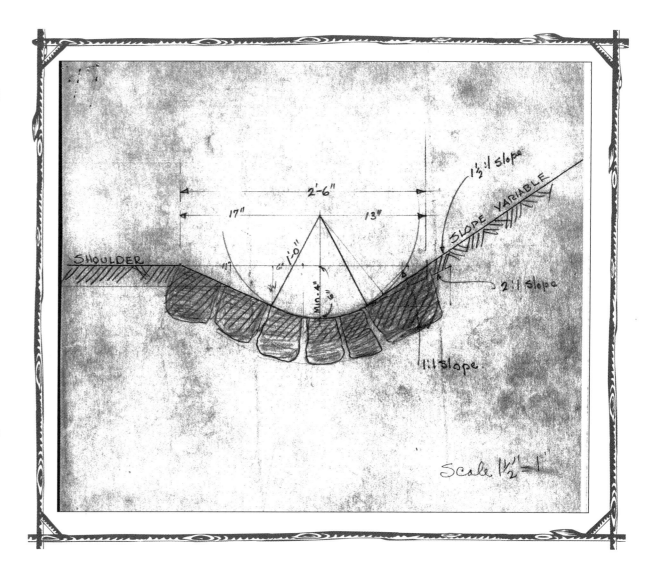

ILLUSTRATION 28: Benson Stone Gutter Design

This sketch drawn by Shenandoah National Park Resident Landscape Architect Benson, although modified by BPR, became the basis for the roadway's stone gutters. Benson's sketch was artistically designed, with a circular center to the ditch defined by the 1' radius shown. BRP modified the plan to make it more practical for field construction.

drawing proposed by BPR "while slightly different from the one proposed by you, is similar. It is two and a half feet wide at the top instead of two [a figure] which conforms to our [BPR's] standard road section." [169]

The construction of rock gutters became part of the construction contracts for the southern portion of the Skyline Drive, but above Swift Run Gap the gutters were built by the Civilian Conservation Corps. Over the next five years over 50,000 lineal feet of rock gutters were built along the Skyline Drive. Because the gutters were meant only to prevent erosion of the soil, the stones were set on a bed of crushed stone and gravel, not concrete, and only mortared in place. They were intended to appear almost natural and be the minimal artificial structural solution to the problem of great quantities of water over short periods of time. One need only look at the asphalt or concrete gutters adjacent to most modern roads to see how successful the Benson/Austin solution was.

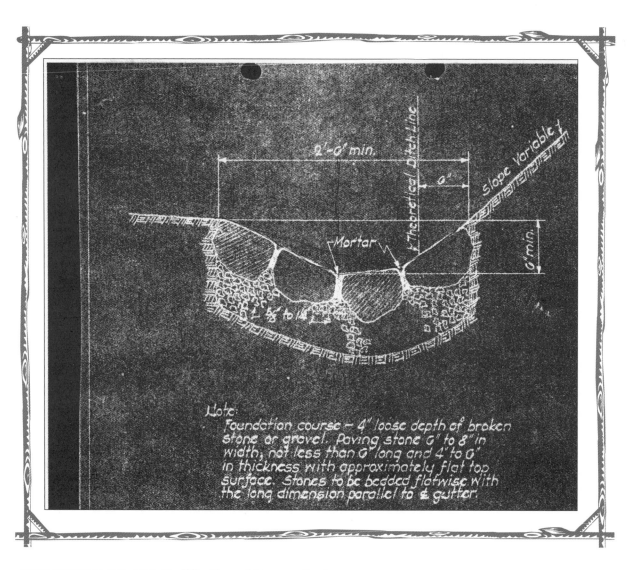

ILLUSTRATION 29: BPR Modification of Benson Design

Austin's redesign of Benson's sketch shows a more pragmatic approach to the problem. By reducing Benson's suggested number of rocks to form the gutter, BPR felt their design would "prevent the smearing of the face of the gutter stones with grout [mortar]" because there would be less jointing involved. Austin suggested this would "add greatly to the appearance of the gutter." [170]

PHOTOGRAPH 46: CCC Gutter Installation

By the time the NPS landscape architects and the BPR realized that the ditches on the uphill slopes of the Skyline Drive needed "hardening," most of the roadway was completed or under contract. The work of building most of the rock-lined gutters fell to the Civilian Conservation Corps. The enrollees quarried the rock, broke it into usable sizes, and laid it according to the specifications developed by the BPR under the supervision of locally employed men (LEMs) with masonry skills hired by the CCC.

PHOTOGRAPH 47: Newly Finished Bank Slope, Stone Gutter, and Drop Inlet

This drop inlet set beside the uphill cut slope catches the water flowing in the stone gutter. The inlets were designed to be set as far into the slope as possible and their covers designed to hold earth. Within a few years the tops of the inlets were covered with grass and perennials, rendering them almost invisible.

Drainage Structures

Rainwater and snowmelt flow downhill, as does water from mountain springs and seeps, but the construction of the Skyline Drive interrupted the age-old downhill flow in the Blue Ridge Mountains. Road drainage, like plumbing in a house, is a necessity, but at best predictably functional and unseen. Ditches and stone gutters intercepted that flow at the base of the uphill cut slope adjacent to the side of the road, but the water had to be moved under the roadway and released on the fill slope below. Ditches and gutters, then and now, normally drain into metal culvert pipes laid under the road, typically with exposed ends. When water flow is substantial, ditches or gutters typically drain into concrete drop inlets such as those seen on any city or village street. When flow is less, open catch basins collect and feed storm water into the culverts. With these necessary utilitarian structures, storm water is controlled and prevented from undermining roads.

The construction specifications by the BPR for the first section of the Skyline Drive provided only for the installation of culvert pipes in low areas that would be filled to provide the road with the desired gradient of 6%. The National Park Service landscape architects did not like the appearance of the exposed roadside culverts, but it was not until 1933 and the hiring of new designers with CCC and WPA funding that serious attention was given to the aesthetics of drainage structures.

The construction drawings for the Front Royal to Panorama portion of the Skyline Drive included many detailed plans and sections for drop inlets and catch basins to render these structures as unobtrusive as possible or to make them seem as if they were a part of the mountain. The concrete drop inlet covers were designed to be set as far as possible into the uphill slope; they had concrete covers designed to be covered with soil and which had front edges with the minimum thickness required for structural soundness. The design assured that, in time, the drop inlet would be covered with vegetation and would appear only as a black slot on the mountain slope.

Catch basins were treated differently. Because they had no covers and could not be set into the slope, they were built of ashlar masonry using the stone from the area. Four types were designed for the Skyline Drive and eventually were used throughout Shenandoah National Park. A simple straight masonry headwall, parallel to the road, through which the culvert passed, was used to drain grass ditches with modest water flow. An "L" shape, with the long side parallel to the road, was specified when drainage was only from one direction and, generally, was being carried by a stone gutter. Two parallel stone walls, parallel to the Skyline Drive, were used when stone gutters fed into the catch basin from both sides. Finally, the most interesting architecturally was a semi-circular stone catch basin designed to collect drainage not only from an adjacent gutter but also from the downhill flow from a spring or small valley.

These simple utilitarian structures are illustrative of the care and concern that went into the creation of the most basic features along the Skyline Drive.

Drinking Fountains

Today bottles of designer water kept cold by travelers in disposable Styrofoam coolers are commonplace. Few of us remember when urban tap water was unpalatable and suspected, often correctly, of harboring disease. From Colonial times, rural communities and charitable organizations built spring boxes and roadside water taps, often in increasingly elaborate monuments, walls, and enclosures, to provide water to passersby and their horses. Travelers learned the locations of public water sources and came to expect them when on the road. Urban travelers loved the taste of "pure" spring water once automobiles became common, and many would use their "Sunday Drive" to bring back bottles from the harnessed roadside springs. [171] Early visitors to the Skyline Drive expected that drinking water would be provided along the route.

Yet the National Park Service landscape architects in the West had had little experience in designing drinking fountains in mountain environments except in areas with major developments, and no standardized designs for fountains had been developed. It fell to Shenandoah National Park's landscape architects to do so.

The installation of drinking fountains along the Skyline Drive was not just a matter of tying into an existing water line—there were no water lines along the roadway. Drilling a well to provide water was not an option; there was no electricity to run well pumps except at Skyland, Big Meadows, and by 1939 at Lewis Mountain and Dickey Ridge. Mountain springs had to be harnessed in traditional spring boxes and gravity-fed by pipes to the fountains. By 1935, as overlooks were being designed and constructed along the sections of the Skyline Drive that had already been built or were being planned, drinking fountains where good springs existed were being retrofitted or made part of the new designs. And each individual fountain was a studied part of the overall landscape design.

By December 1935 Harvey Benson was Shenandoah National Park's Resident Landscape Architect, having shifted from being a CCC employee. On December 31 he wrote to Thomas Vint, NPS Chief Architect, about his plans for fountains:

Hazel Mountain Drinking Fountain

A spring located about 500 yards [from the overlook under construction] presents a good source of supply and is located high enough to feed the fountain by gravity flow. On the attached photos is shown the retaining [wall] in which it is proposed to construct the fountain so that it would be an integral part of the wall and not be too conspicuous to compete with the large boulder [left in place during construction and] protruding from the wall . . . .

<u>Hemlock Springs Drinking Fountain</u>

The location of this fountain is in the existing parking area . . . just south of Hughes River Gap. The small roadside widening was created in order to supply drinking water from the fine spring 100 yards south. The guardwall, walk, and curb have been constructed as shown on the attached photo and the plan proposes the construction of the fountain in the guardwall.

<u>Log Drinking Fountain (for picnic and campgrounds)</u>

This fountain is proposed for immediate construction in Sexton Knoll [Pinnacles] and South River Picnic Grounds. Projects for both areas have been approved for the [CCC] Sixth Period [March-September, 1936].

It seems the log construction is the correct type because it is more in keeping with the surrounding in both areas. [172]

The Civilian Conservation Corps built many of the turned chestnut log fountains, painstakingly boring holes though logs and shaping recesses in the tops for the basin. Although Benson had specified a bronze lining for the fountain top to keep the wood dry, the log fountains were not able to withstand the mountain climate. Within three years a new standard design for fountains in picnic grounds and campgrounds had been developed: a huge locally obtained boulder, drilled and with its top shaped to accept the metal fountain bubbler and basin. This became the standard design for Shenandoah developed areas. In more formal areas stacked and mortared stone fountains were used.

It is in retrospect remarkable that the landscape architects spent so much time designing, and the Civilian Conservation Corps such effort constructing, such minor structures. Today fountains are typically graceless stainless steel posts in barren plazas and are taken for granted as necessary but artless things. It was not always so.

To Pave or Not To Pave

The original road surface of the Skyline Drive was true macadam (See TABLE 4, page 104): 4"-5" of graduated stone with no asphaltic binder or surface treatment. Although there was discussion in 1932 of applying road tar to the crushed stone surface, this brought criticism from some:

Inclosed [sic] is a clipping (*Washington Star*, Sunday, Oct. 23, 1932) that reads like an alibi for an inexcusable breach of good road building practice on the part of interested persons. Better that the Skyline Drive never be opened than that of any part if its surface should be covered with tar. If tar is allowed to cover any part of this drive it will inevitably mean the unnecessary injury and death of many of your constituents.

Moisture on a tar surface makes a road as slippery as ice and automobile brakes become useless. Present knowledge of road building makes it entirely unnecessary to have any road surface that is slippery when wet . . . .

I understand from the inclosed [sic] that it is the deliberate intention with full knowledge on the part of those perpetrating it, to prepare a death trap for many of our unsuspecting and innocent citizens. [173]

Since funding for the application of road tar was not forthcoming, the predicted carnage mercifully was avoided. In 1935 and again the following year, the BPR and NPS threw caution to the wind and applied a coating of tarmacadam (crushed stone mixed on-site with asphaltic emulsion) to the surface of the Skyline Drive from Big Meadows to Skyland.

In 1935 as the Skyland to Big Meadows section of the roadway was being treated, Charles Peterson wrote to Benson: "I would like very much to see the Parking Areas along the Skyline Drive paved along with the Drive itself. Perhaps some of the roads within the picnic areas should be left surfaced more informally with crushed rock. What do you think about that?" [174] Benson wrote back to Peterson:

It seems practical to pave the roadside parking areas in the same manner that the Skyline Drive is treated. But areas such as Jewell Hollow and Crescent Rock Overlook, which are more exclusively developed and are recessed and secluded from the main drive, should, I believe, be treated more informally as to harmonize with the surroundings. The present grey [sic] and green crushed stone surface matches very well with the guard walls, retaining walls, and natural rock outcroppings. The effect would be destroyed if treated with a bituminous material . . . . it seems that a water-bound macadam made from the present crushed stone material would perhaps meet the requirements of the two parking overlooks as well as the picnic ground

PHOTOGRAPH 48: Hazel Mountain Overlook Fountain

The Hazel Mountain Overlook was under construction by the CCC in August 1935. The "large boulder" mentioned by Benson in his letter to Vint is seen in the upper left of the photo, with stone walls being constructed to meet it. The fountain Benson proposed was built in 1936 into the wall shown constructed, to the left of the boulder, in this photograph.

PHOTOGRAPH 49: CCC Making Log Fountains

The Civilian Conservation Corps turned logs on a lathe, augured their length to allow the insertion of water pipes, and shaped their upper surface for the installation of the drinking fountain basin and bubbler. This photograph was taken at the Big Meadows CCC maintenance area in 1936 and indicates the large number of fountains that had been made. The log fountains were soon replaced with boulder or stacked and mortared stone fountains—the log design, although rustic, was just not practical.

PHOTOGRAPH 50: Finished Fountains

This photograph taken at Big Meadows CCC camp ca. 1936 shows an assortment of wood fountains in varied states of completion. That to the lower right is essentially completed, having been fitted with its bronze basin; that to the upper right has yet to be turned on the lathe.

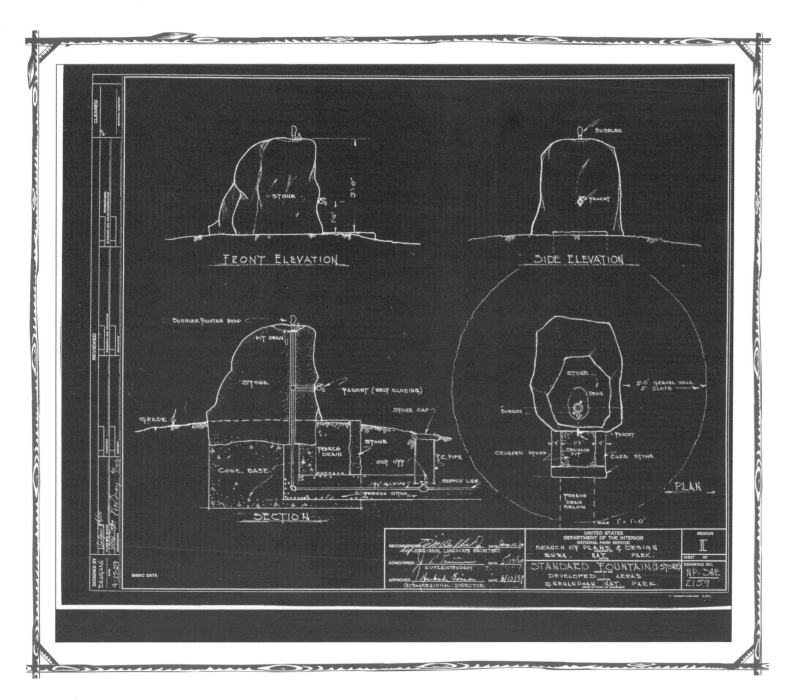

**ILLUSTRATION 30:
Standard Boulder
Drinking Fountain
Design**

After it was obvious that
chestnut logs would not be
practical as fountains in the
Blue Ridge Mountains, NPS
landscape architects designed a
standard boulder fountain that
would stand the test of time.
These fountains first were used
in the more informal picnic
grounds and campgrounds, but
also at less architecturally
formal overlooks.

road. Mr. Lassiter does not agree with the water-bound macadam idea or with leaving the picnic ground roads finished with just a crushed rock surface. [175]

Peterson wrote to Lassiter that he was against bituminous paving in the picnic areas since the roads would then "seem very formal in serving the purposes for which . . . [they] were intended." [176] Lassiter responded in reference to a crushed stone surface in the picnic grounds:

> This type of surface will be hard to maintain due to the pitting and ravelling out of the stone, will be dusty, and will always have a certain amount of loose stone laying on it which will make difficult walking, especially for the ladies who are prone to wear high heel shoes at all times.

> An asphalt treated roadway, finished with [an] excess of [stone] chips will present a stone surface appearance and will eliminate the objection I mentioned. [177]

This was the course that would be followed in the picnic grounds and within the more isolated overlooks and parking areas.

In April 1938 Lassiter wrote to Oliver G. Taylor, Chief Engineer of the National Park Service, protesting that the BPR was planning to apply an asphaltic surface to the Swift Run Gap to Blackrock Gap section of the roadway, a portion not yet completed. The remainder of the Skyline Drive was still not permanently surfaced.

I strongly feel that before more road is surfaced in a temporary makeshift manner, all surfacing money should be applied to the northern and central sections of the Drive in order to give a satisfactory surface both from the riding and maintenance standpoint.

The surfacing on both the northern and central sections, with the exception of nine miles in the middle of the central section, consists of a mixed-in-place wearing surface that is extremely open and which has deteriorated during this past winter . . . . On the nine-mile section above mentioned, a contract has been let

PHOTOGRAPH 51: Tarmacadam Installation

Tarmacadam is a mixture of asphalt emulsion (road tar) and gravel applied to a road surface, rolled in place, topped with fine gravel, and again rolled. Unlike today's plant-mixed asphalt, which is brought to the site and applied hot, tarmacadam was applied cold. It produced a smooth but quite porous surface not long-lived under heavy traffic use.

and work will begin soon on the application of a 2-inch plant-mixed surface which should give us a very satisfactory job . . . . For the balance of the 55 miles, it is urgently requested that a 1-inch plant-mix be applied, which will give us a tight, water-proof, smooth surface and which will protect and prolong the life of the investment we now have in this road. [178]

Taylor sent a memorandum to Chief Landscape Architect Vint three days after receiving Lassiter's letter. He agreed with the Superintendent that the south district paving should be deferred and funding used in "providing some improvement on the roads now open to heavy traffic." [179]

By the time the southern section of the Skyline Drive opened to the public on August 29, 1939, the entire roadway had been paved with plant-mixed asphalt, providing a smooth and maintainable riding surface for the 270,833 automobiles that traveled over it that year. [180]

Vegetation, Revegetation, and Devegetation

It is remarkable that, in a project to build a 105-mile road through a significantly forested area, landscape architects were concerned with saving individual trees. NPS Eastern Division Assistant Landscape Architect Ludgate wrote to his supervisor, Charles Peterson, from Skyland on July 27, 1931 (before construction was to begin on the central section of the Skyline Drive):

> I have talked to all four [of BPR's field supervisors] and tried to impress on them the necessity for avoiding damage to trees through carelessness. I have recommended that any sizable trees which come within the fill slopes to the extent of being covered six feet from the [existing] ground be saved. These can be protected by means of a dry wall, or by sub drainage with means of vitrified tile. Care is being taken in the burning of trees and brush [cut down] on the right of way to avoid burning the live foliage at the sides. [181]

When Ludgate inspected the completed work in September 1932 one of his general recommendations, supported by the NPS Director, was that "all trees damaged by contractors should be carefully trimmed and scars painted with black paint. All dead branches should be removed." [182]

The following June, Peterson wrote to BPR's Bishop stating that the following paragraph should be inserted into the "Special Provisions" portion of the standard road construction specifications:

> Trees and shrubs of value to the appearance of the road, and coming within the fill slopes to a point where the trunks are covered to a maximum depth of five feet, shall be left upon order of the Engineer. These trees shall be protected as directed by the Engineer, and any special protection work required - will be paid for as "Extra Work." [183]

Since the BPR, not the NPS, was the official contractor for the construction, its engineer was the official who dealt with the contractor. However, it was understood that the NPS landscape architects would determine the "trees and shrubs of value."

But saving trees during construction of the northern and southern portions of the roadway was not the only concern of the landscape architects. Over and over again, Rogers and Harriss noted special stands of specific species, typically mountain laurel (*Kalmia latifolia*), that they wanted the Civilian Conservation Corps to salvage before the steam shovels moved into an area. These salvaged plants were to be heeled in at the CCC nurseries at Big Meadows and Front Royal until they could be replanted on the completed cut-and-fill slopes. Harriss noted particularly outstanding mountain laurel to be salvaged near milepost 13 in the north district of the park. Landscape architect Rogers discussed the "center of the Laurel Planting Area" between Jewell Hollow Overlook and Stony Man Overlook, a stretch of the Skyline Drive now known for outstanding displays of laurel blooms each year. [184]

Planting of slopes was not a random affair. Slope blending, as previously discussed, was an important consideration to the landscape architects. When cut-and-fill slopes occurred in areas with a dense shrubby understory, heavy plantings of shrubs were installed. In more open locations, the banks were lined with strips of sod lifted from meadows and pastures where facility development was to occur. The intent was always to have the newly created topography blend into the surrounding area with the passage of time.

As the construction for the roadway and the developed area picnic grounds, waysides, campgrounds, and concession facilities reached fruition in 1938-1939, less native plant material was available for salvage. The worst cases of roadside erosion had been corrected, and the landscape architects shifted their efforts to one of enhancing the natural landscape as opposed to stabilizing it.

Harlan Kelsey, one of the original members of the Southern Appalachian National Park Committee, owner of a native plant nursery, and a "Collaborator at Large" for the National Park Service, became actively involved in the evolving landscape along the Skyline Drive. In a letter to Director Arno B. Cammerer discussing his two-day visit to the park with Frederick Law Olmsted, Kelsey stated:

> Last week in discussing the Skyline Drive with . . . Olmsted, he remarked that after 30 miles or so, to him the trip became a little bit monotonous.
>
> The forst [*sic*] landscape, it must be admitted, is more or less monotonously the same throughout the Park, and this, of course, is occasioned by the fact that all the land has been cut over, not only once, but probably in many cases many times . . . .

PHOTOGRAPH 52: Building the Skyline Drive

In many forested sections of the mountain, a significant number of the trees were dead or dying chestnuts, as here shown, but were interspersed with living trees of other species. The contractors initially cut a narrow terrace into the slope ahead of their machinery, moving the cut earth and rock ahead and downhill to fill and build up the rough road path they would follow. The future park's landscape architects wanted to save as many as possible of the large viable trees on the downhill fill slope, and designed tree wells and, initially, aeration systems to preserve them in place.

[In] the northern area of the Park, originally there was unmistakably a dominance of White Pine and Chestnut . . . . This indicates that there should be many thousands of White Pines planted in that area . . . .

Again, from time to time along the Skyland [*sic*] Drive we find areas where Canada Hemlock once flourished in the upper ends of ravines . . . . These remnants indicate that once there was [*sic*] considerable areas of hemlocks in those places which, if restored, will give a very distinctive and pleasant relief from the excessfully [*sic*] dominant hardwood forest.

. . . [as to] the splendid areas completely, or quite so, covered with Muntainlaurel [*sic*], and in other places, Azaleas or a combination of both which are now being choked out and their development impeded by an overgrowth of weedy deciduous trees and shrubs . . . judicious cutting should be done to develop these areas into fairly pure stands of the variety which deserved dominance. This would again tend to relieve monotony of landscape. [185]

Kelsey closed by strongly advocating continued use of vines on the slopes, particularly "Virginia Clematis, Bittersweet . . . native grapevines, and Virginia Creeper . . . as they will trail from 50 to 100 feet in many cases."

The plan of Kelsey and the national park and CCC landscape architects was essentially one of gardening on a very grand scale, remaking everything on, near, or visible from the roadway into a designed composition of alternating and created variety. Today this viewpoint is anathema to National Park Service resource managers, but it was a time when the science of ecology barely existed, natural vegetative communities were little understood, and the Service did not have a basic policy for natural resource management. The NPS designed nature as contrasted to designing with nature. Kelsey, owner of a native plant nursery, typified this viewpoint when he stated:

> Again let me urge that the plant materials used should be practically one hundred percent native material and where exotics are used, *they should be those that cannot be told from the native material by the average observer* [emphasis added by author]. Probably this is all arranged for but I think it so important that I know you won't mind my mentioning it again. [186]

A 1939 survey of the CCC nursery at Big Meadows made by CCC Landscape Architect Knox indicated that it held 4,500 Virginia creeper (*Parthenocissus quinquefolia*), 1,526 trumpet creeper (*Campsis radicans*), 116 bittersweet (*Celastrus scandens*), 138 arrow-wood (*Viburnum dentatum*), 64 alternate-leaved dogwood (*Cornus alternifolia*), 56 sumac (*Rhus canadensis*), and substantial numbers of pitch pine, red spruce, fir, walnut, and rosebay (*Rhododendron maximum*). [187] Between July 1939 and June 1940 Shenandoah's CCC camps planted 26, 701 trees and shrubs, a figure far beyond the capacity of the camp nurseries to produce. [188] The CCC intensified their efforts to collect native seed to grow their own plants and also increased the purchase of materials from governmental or commercial nurseries. In March 1940, 10,000 two-foot tall white pines were ordered from the Virginia Forest Service and 5,000 pitch pines were bought from the Cole Nursery Company, Painesville, Ohio, in September. In fact, from 1939 onward most of the plants used by the CCC were grown outside the park, and often outside the Commonwealth of Virginia.

Although the Civilian Conservation Corps camps closed by June 1942, the work of landscape revegetation and aesthetic improvement was continued through April 1945 by the efforts of the CPS (Civilian Public Service) work program, established for conscientious objectors during World War II. A "Summary of Field Planting" produced in that month indicated that 650 Table Mountain pines had been planted at the former Skyland CCC camp, 25 at Hawksbill Gap, 450 at Hawksbill-Heywood Saddle, and 150 at Spitler Knoll. Pitch pines had been planted at South River (150), Kites Deadening (100), 50 at the former Bald Face CCC camp (NP-3), and 75 at Naked Creek. [189]

As the left hand of the CCC added vegetation, the right hand took it away. From January 1937 to January 1939 (a representative period), the CCC camps in the park cleared 74 forested acres along the Skyline Drive to provide drive-by views of the Piedmont and the Shenandoah Valley, or to increase the vistas available at overlooks and parking areas. The acreage cleared in only these two years of the CCC's nine-year existence has to be placed in context: the entire 100' wide right-of-way for the

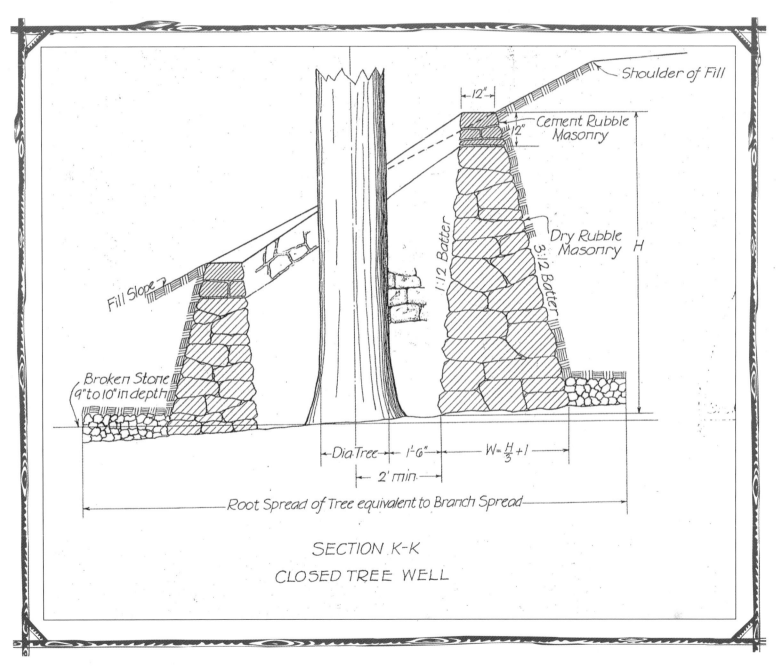

Shoulder of Fill

—12"—

12"

Cement Rubble
Masonry

1:12 Batter

3:12 Batter

Dry Rubble
Masonry

H

Fill Slope

Broken Stone
(9"to 10" in depth

—Dia.Tree— 1'-6" $W = \frac{H}{3} + 1$

— 2' min.—

—Root Spread of Tree equivalent to Branch Spread—

SECTION K-K
CLOSED TREE WELL

ILLUSTRATION 31:
Tree Well Design

By the time the drawings and specifications for the construction of the Front Royal to Panorama section of the Skyline Drive were ready to go to contract, they included this detail for the construction of a dry-laid masonry tree well to protect trees deemed significant by the park's landscape architects. Not only did the tree well protect the trunk of the trees, but with an added 9"-10" layer of crushed stone on existing grade downhill from the proposed fill slope within the root zone, it provided aeration to the tree roots after fill was installed. A considerable number of these wells were built; some are still visible today, including the one just south of, and adjacent to, the Browntown Overlook. [190]

PHOTOGRAPH 53: Tree Wells at Panorama

These two dry-laid stone tree wells were built adjacent to the Skyline Drive near the intersection with Highway # 211. The buildings in the background may be the Cliser House, gas station, and barn that were removed once the park was officially established in December 1935.

PHOTOGRAPH 54: CCC-planted Mountain Laurel

The west side of the Skyline Drive north of Hughes River Gap/Stony Man Overlook and the Corbin Cabin parking area, shown in this photograph, was part of what Rogers called the "Laurel Planting Area," which extended north to the Pinnacles Picnic Grounds. These small laurel transplants were salvaged from locations to be excavated for road construction, planted in CCC nurseries, and later used both to rectify erosion and to beautify areas. Note that at the time of this photograph, possibly late 1933, the roadbed was unpaved and no stone ditches had been established.

**PHOTOGRAPH 55:
CCC Planting Potted
Perennials**

Native vines were a favorite with the park's landscape architects. Both transplanted and purchased from commercial nurseries, they were planted along the walls and slopes. In this view a Civilian Conservation Corps enrollee is planting both Virginia creeper (*Parthenocissus quinquefolia*) and trumpet creeper (*Campsis radicans*) on a cut slope above the Skyline Drive. Harlan Kelsey, NPS Collaborator at Large, advocated just such placement of vines.

PHOTOGRAPH 56: Sod Strips On Graded Bank

In less forested and more open locations along the Skyline Drive, the CCC cut shallow trenches and planted long strips of sod lifted from meadow or pasture areas slated for facility development or, in other locations, rye grass sod strips. These were mulched with weeds and would in time develop into broad mats of native grasses and wildflowers. Many of the open road shoulders along the roadway today were originally established in this manner. After the forest fire of 2000 burned broad areas between Panorama and Skyland, lineal patterns were evident in the burnt perennials along some of the road shoulders, ghostly traces of their original planting patterns.

PHOTOGRAPH 57: Big Tree Transplanted for Park Headquarters

The work of the Civilian Conservation Corps was not limited to the removal of sod, shrubs, and saplings. On occasion, the enrollees salvaged large specimen trees to replant them in prominent locations in developed areas. This pine was transplanted to the park headquarters in Luray.

construction of the Skyline Drive in Shenandoah National Park was equal to 1,189 acres. The CCC was clearing an average of 3% of that total, by hand, every year for landscape enhancement.

From the beginning, the Civilian Conservation Corps worked on creating views and vistas. Occasionally the work required total clear-cutting of the forest; in other cases only modest pruning and brush removal were required. Typical are these entries in a letter from C. V. Bert, Superintendent of CCC Camp NP- 3 (Bald Face) to Landscape Architect Rogers:

> #6. Station 634 50.Large oak stands, prune. Clear out witch hazel and brush on top. Cut trees notched [marked for removal] below.

> #7. Station 617 0. Leave large oaks, head up. Take out marked trees and high shrubs. Splendid view under trees traveling south. Not a parking overlook.

> #9. Station 564. View to east. Leave and head up large oak. Cut out all high trees and locust. Butternut trees on north and south end of vista. Not a complete view. Not a parking overlook.

> #12. Station 478. Recommend we cut out vista here. Just as start up mountain. About 4 oak will do it. We need some view in this vicinity.

> #15. Station 342 25. Not a parking out look. Take out 3 large oak and 1 birch. Does not help view but composition.

> #16. Station 301. Not a parking overlook. Good view. A great deal of dead and tall trees [have been notched] to come out. [191]

Bert was just one of the many CCC Camp Superintendents. All actively examined every foot of their portion of the Skyline Drive, looking for good existing views that they could improve or searching for obstructed vistas that they could have the CCC boys open to provide new and varied views for the traveler. This vegetative tinkering continued until 1945.

More Than a Road

Assistant Landscape Architect, Eastern Division, V. Russell Ludgate wrote to Charles Peterson in July 1931:

> With only one hundred feet of right-of-way on the line, picnic and parking areas will be almost impossible to construct under the present contract, but topography will be taken where study is necessary, and plans considered for building them later on when sufficient land has been obtained. [192]

Ludgate summarized a problem that would haunt Shenandoah National Park for decades. For the first five years the roadway was the park, and for many years to come—long after the park was established—many travelers never realized they were in a national park at all.

In 1929 the National Park Service first required the production of park development plans for new units of the system.

> Such a plan will give the general picture of the park showing the circulation system (roads and trails), the communication system (telephone and telegraph), Wilderness areas and Developed areas. More detailed plans of developed areas will be required to properly portray these special features. These plans being general guides will naturally be constantly in a state of development and should be brought up to date and made a matter of record annually. Their success depends upon the proper collaboration of the study and effect on the part of the park Superintendent, the Landscape Architect, the Chief Engineer, and the Sanitary Engineer. The resulting plan will not be the work of any one but will include the work of all. Since Park Development is primarily a Landscape development, these plans will be coordinated by the Landscape Division. [193]

The production of a Master Plan was mandatory to guide the careful development of a park. In the case of Shenandoah, the rush to create the road superseded park planning. Cammerer wrote to Albright late in 1932 recommending that

> early next spring the entire area from Front Royal to Waynesboro should be carefully studied by our landscape and engineering forces with the view of preparing a map on which available water sources for drinking, sanitary, and culinary purposes are located, desirable camp, hotel and lodge grounds indicated, so that a development project map for the entire area may

be prepared as a basis for study of essential public service installation. [194]

Cammerer's wish for a master development plan was not acted upon until establishment of the Civilian Conservation Corps and the Public Works Administration provided funding for landscape architects for the Skyline Drive and the proposed park. Landscape architects Rogers and Harriss, once they arrived in 1933, were able to initiate planning for facility development in the north and south districts before those sections of the Skyline Drive were built. But planning for the central section of the roadway occurred after the fact. And few of the plans could be implemented until the park was actually established in December 1935.

The first Shenandoah National Park Master Plan was produced in 1935 and was regularly revised through 1942, with no revision produced in 1941. The first plans were sterling examples of optimistic over-development. Fourteen major developed areas were to be built, with larger areas to include cabin colonies, campgrounds, and picnic areas at Skyland, Big Meadows, Blackrock, Hogback Mountain, Bear Wallow Springs, Loft Mountain, and Hogwallow Flats. Smaller developments, including only gas stations, campsites, picnic grounds, and lunch stands, were planned for Gravel Springs, Pinnacles, Dickey Ridge, Calvary Rocks, Ivy Creek, South River, and Comers Deadening. Significant construction was to occur almost every eight miles along the full length of the Skyline Drive. Skyland was to be rehabilitated by the construction of a large new lodge, a new coffee shop, and 144 new cabins. Big Meadows was similarly to be developed.

In the same year the CCC landscape architects were busily developing plans for Shenandoah National Park that could have accommodated the needs of the population of a small city on vacation, Secretary of the Interior Harold Ickes was putting the brakes on such development. In a speech to the National Park Service Conference of State Park Authorities, he expressed his concerns that abundant CCC labor was damaging the national parks:

> The recreational needs of the country are one of the major problems of the country. It seems to me there is a clear distinction between what we are trying to do and ought to do in our National Parks and what we ought to do in at least the State and local parks . . . . our National Parks, so far as possible, ought to be kept in their natural state . . . . I am not in favor of doing anything along the lines of so-called improvements that we do not have to do . . . . I am not willing that our beautiful areas should be opened up to people who are either too old to walk, as I am, or too lazy to walk, as a great many young people are who ought to be ashamed of themselves. I do not happen to favor the scarring of the wonderful mountainside just so we can say we have a skyline drive. It sounds poetical, but it may be creating a natural atrocity . . . .

> So long as I am Secretary of the Interior and have anything to say about the parks, I am going to use all of the influence I have to keep parks just as far as possible in their natural state. Your State Parks are a different problem. They are more recreational than wilderness areas. [195]

It took a few years for the Secretary's beliefs to work down to park level, but the Master Plans as ultimately implemented were far more modest. Skyland, Dickey Ridge, Big Meadows, and Lewis Mountain became multi-use developments with cabins, campgrounds (excepting Dickey Ridge), picnic grounds, and restaurants. Waysides with restaurants and gas stations were built at Big Meadows and Elkwallow. Additional picnic grounds were built at Pinnacles, South River, and Elkwallow, but these were greatly simplified and the original plans for lunch stands eliminated. Only road circulation, comfort stations, fire pits, drinking fountains, and landscape furniture were constructed. The shelter at Pinnacles Picnic Grounds was an exception to the rule.

The landscape design of the developed areas is beyond the scope of this book, but it should be said that each was carefully studied by the park landscape architects. Detailed topographic maps showing all significant trees and shrubs, by type and size, were produced. Areas were selected with water available for drinking and comfort stations. Designs capitalized on existing features such as rock outcrops, vistas, or specimen trees. Roads were consistently one-way to minimize their width and reduce the impact of construction and paving. Artificial structures, whether fire pits, picnic tables, benches, or comfort stations, were carefully designed to blend with their surroundings.

119

Each individual item and each larger area had a requisite architectural drawing that needed approval both by the park Superintendent and by the National Park Service Washington staff.

The lodges, cabins, waysides, and campstores in developed areas were designed and built by the Virginia Sky-Line Company, the park concessioner, under the review and approval of the National Park Service. The structures in the picnic grounds and at overlooks and campgrounds were designed by the park landscape architects and built by the Civilian Conservation Corps.

The National Park Service, however, was only beginning to develop a unified and coherent philosophy of design as Shenandoah was being built. Frank A. Waugh's seminal work, *Landscape Conservation: Planning for the Restoration, Conservation, and Utilization of Wild Lands for Park and Forest Recreation*, was not published by the National Park Service until August 1935. The three-volume landscape structure design handbook, *Park and Recreation Structures* by Albert H. Good, followed in 1938. Both publications became the touchstones for park design for decades to come; both were to come too late for Shenandoah's early efforts. But Waugh's basic premise that "artificial structures in wild park lands should be made as inconspicuous as possible, and should be constructed of native materials such as local stone, peeled logs, etc." [196] was derived from almost a century of development of the philosophy of rustic landscape design.

Shenandoah's landscape architects looked to local vernacular design for their inspiration. As had George Freeman Pollock at Skyland before them, they borrowed architectural details from the cabins of the mountain residents displaced by park creation. They used the materials the earlier residents had used: chestnut logs, wood shingles, and stone from the surrounding mountains. They found inspiration in the historic scale and size of windows, in the typical board and batten doors and wrought iron door hinges, and in the traditional steep roof pitches. Although more modern methods of manufacture were used, and in some cases more modern materials, the buildings created were remarkably sensitive both to their surroundings and to the historic context of the park.

In 1940 Shenandoah National Park Resident Landscape Architect Harvey Benson wrote:

Five years ago Pinnacles Picnic Grounds . . . was developed and made ready for use. Parking accommodations for 170 cars, 20 fire places, 100 tables, five water fountains and a standard comfort station, together with water and sanitary system, were installed by the CCC. Since this first recreation development others have been followed in rapid succession due to the overwhelming demands made on the park by the increasing travel on Skyline Drive. South River Picnic Grounds . . . was developed and opened in 1935. Picnic developments followed at Elkwallow, Dickey Ridge and Big Meadows. Total picnicking facilities installed to date include parking space for 715 automobiles, 95 fire places, 350 tables, 30 water fountains and six comfort stations. [197]

Landscape architect Benson left his position in March 1942 to accept a position with the War Department at the Richmond General Depot for the duration of the war. [198] The last CCC enrollees left the park in June and with them the park's remaining landscape architects and engineers. Soon gas would be rationed and visitation would slow to a trickle. The concessioner closed its new facilities. Eleven years after it started, the development and planning for the Skyline Drive and the park came to an end. America was at war.

With the end of the war, attempts to design the Skyline Drive and the park landscape at God-scale ceased. The landscape architects were gone. The engineers absent. The huge labor force non-existent. The Skyline Drive and the park were, to a great extent, left to nature's forces.

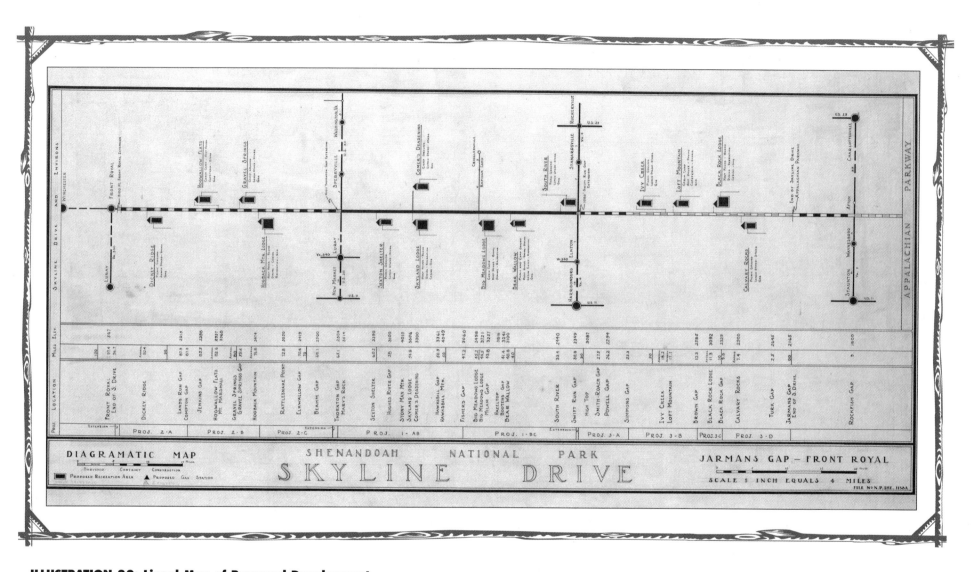

ILLUSTRATION 32: Lineal Map of Proposed Development

Produced as part of the 1936 Master Plan, this straight-line representation of the Skyline Drive shows the numbers and types of developed areas first proposed for the park. Secretary of the Interior Harold Ickes ended such grandiose planning for the National Park Service. The Mission '66 program, established 20 years later to revitalize the parks for a new generation of visitors, resurrected many of the original plans for Shenandoah National Park rejected by Ickes.

PHOTOGRAPH 58: Visitor Contact Station at Crescent Rock Overlook

The Civilian Conservation Corps erected this building at Crescent Rock Overlook (ca. 1936) to serve as a visitor information station. A similar structure was built at Hughes River Gap/Stony Man Overlook. A casual imitation of mountain cabin construction, the small structure used the rounded face slabs left over from sawing logs (probably dead chestnut trees) to create the exterior walls, a practical application of waste materials and one that approximated log construction. The roof was covered with wood shingles, probably sawn at the Skyland CCC camp sawmill.

PHOTOGRAPH 59: Standard Shenandoah National Park Comfort Station

Waugh's basic premise that "artificial structures should be built from native materials" was a guideline, at least in appearance, in Shenandoah National Park. Extreme care was taken to design buildings along the Skyline Drive using the materials at hand and being sensitive to the local vernacular architecture. As the park was overburdened with dead chestnut trees and there was no shortage of rock, this was the palette of materials with which the landscape architects worked to create new buildings. This comfort station, i.e., public toilet, at Big Meadows followed the standard design created for the park, based on local pattern. However, the "hand hewn" logs were first sawn at the CCC sawmills and then hewn with adzes for effect. CCC handmade concrete tiles, closely simulating wood shingles, were to replace the sawn wood shingles used on this and the earliest structures, a concession to the hazard of forest fires.

PHOTOGRAPH 60: Entrance Station at Rockfish Gap

Once it was mandated that a 25-cent fee would be charged to travel on the Skyline Drive, entrance stations had to be constructed to collect tolls. The entrance station at Rockfish Gap was typical. Everything in the building, except for the iron in the strap hinges on the doors, the nails holding the shingles, the glass in the sash, and the iron flagpole, was likely of local origin. The chestnut log guardrails, the stone wall, and the wood for the shingles and siding were obtained by the CCC within the park. The building is an interpretation of local vernacular design.

Epilogue

For all intents and purposes, the national parks became the federal budget stepchildren for the decade following WWII. Staffs and funding were flat and resources minimally maintained. The National Park Service had 5,145 employees in June 1941, but only 1,795 in June 1946. [199] But visitation to the parks was again growing at record numbers. Shenandoah Superintendent Freeland wrote of the condition of the postwar Skyline Drive in 1946:

The forest returned so fast the first thing we knew we were just driving through a green tunnel. We realized we had to do some vista clearing. So we called the Virginia Forest Service and our landscape people . . . and had some meetings and surveyed the whole area from Front Royal to Rockfish and outlined on the plans just where the vista clearing should be done . . . .

We had objections to that from various sources. They said, "you let the trees grow and then you go and cut them . . . ." Of course these areas were only where there were overlooks–and there's no sense having an overlook if you

couldn't see anything . . . . Devereux Butcher [Editor of the National Parks Association magazine] . . . . was one of those objecting to the cutting. [200]

By 1955, in anticipation of the 25th anniversary of the Skyline Drive, the Bureau of Public Roads proposed to rehabilitate the Skyline Drive, focusing mostly on safety improvements. By then most of the wooden guardrails had decayed and many of the ashlar and dry-laid walls were in poor condition. BPR wanted to install modern walls in many locations, some in which no guard structure had ever existed. The Director of the National Park Service, Conrad Wirth, became involved in the issue:

In talking with Director Wirth about your job for guard rail, he tells me that he has recently decided to do all the guard rail jobs in the parks with our own forces. This will involve taking the job away from the Bureau of Public Roads.

Mr. Wirth also feels very strongly that we should continue the same style of guard wall already in use in

Shenandoah. He feels, too, that the amount of guard wall should be held to the bare minimum. [201]

This was part and parcel of Wirth's bold ten-year plan to reinvigorate the national parks by the 50th anniversary of the National Park Service in 1966–"Mission '66." Wirth stated:

Travel has increased to the point of embarrassment, while provision for it and for better protection of both the parks and those who use them has been deferred again and again because of a lack of funds . . . . The system, designed for 25 million visitors a year, is now called on to bear a load that is twice that heavy. [202]

Wirth's Mission '66 campaign was widely publicized and embraced by Congress and the Eisenhower Administration. National Park Service funding skyrocketed. For the first time since 1942, Shenandoah National Park developed a new master plan that to some extent resurrected and incorporated new development as excessive as that proposed in the plans of the 1930s. The plans for new campgrounds at

PHOTOGRAPH 61: View of Big Meadows CCC Camp Showing Dark Hollow Falls Road Curve

Camp NP-2 (Big Meadows) in the summer of 1934. The Skyline Drive, snaking west of the camp, heads north to Dark Hollow to the left; the original extreme curve was eliminated decades later. The chestnut log palisade fence is visible to the right of the mess hall and barracks. A homestead with a substantial barn is located just east (above) the camp.

Mathews Arm and Loft Mountain, expansion of the Big Meadows and Lewis Mountain campgrounds, and the construction of a new visitor center at Big Meadows were implemented. The conversion of the Dickey Ridge Lodge, a concession facility never reopened after WWII, was undertaken. New sewage treatment plants and water supply systems were constructed. New park employee residences—cookie-cutter designs used throughout the country--were built in Luray and Front Royal. But the plans to build visitor centers in each new campground, an additional picnic area and second campground in the north district, two new picnic areas and an additional campground in the south district, and to expand the central district picnic grounds were never implemented due to a lack of funds and a rejection of these plans by the Washington offices as excessive.

The park concessioner embraced the Mission '66 program. The old Skyland cabins along the edge of the plateau were demolished and replaced with modern units more easily maintained and serviced. Similar structures were erected in primary locations along the ridge at Big Meadows. The Panorama Tea Room was razed and replaced with a modern restaurant and gift shop.

The Mission '66 work on the Skyline Drive was not as extensive as the proposed facility development: the road would be resurfaced where necessary; the Marys Rock Tunnel would be lined with concrete in an attempt to deal with the problem of icing; guardwall rehabilitation would continue; the extreme roadway curve at Dark Hollow Falls

would be straightened; new entrance stations would be constructed at Front Royal, Panorama, and Swift Run, and new cloverleaf interchanges built at the latter two entrances. It is doubtful that the original landscape architects for the Skyline Drive would have endorsed most of the Mission '66 construction—it violated many of the basic precepts of early park design. It was not, in most cases, built with native materials, using local vernacular design precedent as a standard. The Mission '66 mantra was efficiency through standardized design throughout the National Park Service. Thus an overpass designed for California could be used, with minor modifications, in Virginia. Rustic park architecture specific and sympathetic to the park itself yielded to repetitive national designs, more conducive to economic need and expediency.

The work on rebuilding the guardwalls on the Skyline Drive, however, continued as Director Wirth had specified, to the extent that the walls were rehabilitated so as to appear as first built:

> Mr. Beer seemed well pleased with the 50 feet of
> reconstructed guardwall with the following exceptions.
>   To have the joints in roadway face of wall to be
> raked [i.e., recessed] deep to a min. of 2 inches.
>   To have the completed top surface of the wall to
> be as near as level as possible.
>   To have joints raked fairly deep on top face of wall.
> Mr. Beer also stated that the Park Service would like to
> have reconstructed guardwalls to resemble the existing
> guardwalls as nearly as possible. [203]

In 1981 the park began the two-year process of writing a *Development Concept Plan/General Management Plan*, which replaced earlier master plans, but also was designed to guide future management decisions. The plan as finalized in 1983 was long on proposals for recreational development and modernization and short on an appreciation of the park's cultural resources. Had the plan been fully implemented, almost all of the historic structures at Skyland would have been demolished and replaced with modern motel-type units and the historic design of Lewis Mountain developed area would have been sacrificed by extensive new cabin construction. The plan did suggest, however, that Massanutten Lodge and the Skyline Drive might be worthy of study for future inclusion into the National Register of Historic Places.

The *General Management Plan* was being drafted at the same time Congress was creating the 1982 Surface Transportation Assistance Act, which would have more impact on the Skyline Drive than any legislation since its creation. The law established the Federal Lands Highway Program (FLHP), funded by the Highway Trust Fund, the recipient of federal gasoline taxes. The purpose of the FLHP was to provide funding for a coordinated program managed by the Federal Highway Administration (FHA)--the successor to the BPR--to maintain and build public roads on federal lands. Once again the highway engineers were in the driver's seat. Their initial surveys of the Skyline Drive led to the recommendation that much of the original stone guardwall, which the engineers felt was unsafe, be removed and replaced with steel guardrail or concrete "Jersey barriers."

It is fortuitous that this proposal was made at the same time the *General Management Plan* was being written. The significance of the Skyline Drive as a historic resource had been recognized by the planning team and the FHA proposal was not favorably received. After extensive and prolonged discussion among all levels of both the NPS and FHA bureaucracies, a compromise was reached in which stone walls with concrete cores would replace the original stone guardwalls. The new walls were to be higher than the originals (27″ compared to the 22″ of many of the originals). The stone of the replaced existing walls was to be cut and applied as a veneer to the new concrete core; in many cases this changed the basic masonry pattern of the wall. Nevertheless, it was a significant achievement in maintaining the essential character of the road.

The major infusion of funding generated by the creation of the FLHP and its potential to destroy the character of many historic park roads and parkways led the National Park Service to establish a Park Road Policy Task Force in 1982. The charge to the group was to define the philosophy and purpose of park roads for the first time since the 1930s. Shenandoah National Park Superintendent Robert Jacobsen served with the group. The draft report by the committee stated:

> The fundamental purpose of the national parks—bringing humankind and the environment into closer harmony—dictates that the quality of the park experience must be our primary concern. Full enjoyment of a national park visit depends on its being a safe and leisurely experience.

The distinctive character of park roads plays a basic role in setting this essential unhurried pace. Consequently, park roads are designed with extreme care and sensitivity with respect to the terrain and environment through which they pass—they are laid lightly onto the land. [204]

The report went on:

> As stated on a brochure that was once given to visitors when they entered National Parks: **Park roads are for leisurely driving only. If you are in a hurry, you might do well to take another route now, and come back when you have more time.** [205]

Between June 1983 and June 2002 the Federal Lands Highway Program coordinated the design and expenditure of over $34,000,000 for rehabilitation of the Skyline Drive. Failing chestnut log gabions and cribbing were replaced. Stone gutters were rebuilt. Fill slopes were reconstructed. Headwalls and drop inlets were reconstructed. Much of this work was done with sensitivity to the historic character of the roadway, although many of the trailhead parking areas constructed based on the recommendations of the *General Management Plan* are, in retrospect, over-designed or intrusive on the historic scene. One failure of the FLHP, however, is that it covered only the rehabilitation costs for the actual roadway and did not provide funding for the overlooks--these have been defined as parking areas and not, therefore, eligible for FLHP *road* funding. For this reason, many of the historic park overlooks are in an advanced state of deterioration.

In 1997 the Skyline Drive was entered into the National Register of Historic Places. Since then, all of the park's developed areas have been studied and found to be of equal national historic significance, not only for landscape design and architectural style highly representative of its time and type, but also because the creation of the Skyline Drive illustrates broad themes in American history—the development of transportation, the rise of middle-class recreation, and the social and economic programs of the Great Depression and the New Deal. The hand-cut walls have stories to tell for those willing to listen.

The Skyline Drive is, however, not a parkway; it is a road in a national park, a corridor through a large natural area. To many travelers the roadway represents only brilliant October foliage. But for those who take the time, or better yet another time, to visit, the Skyline Drive can offer surprising glimpses of wildness: a pair of thirsty ravens drinking from a CCC-built fountain; a bobcat perched regally on a dry-laid wall; a quail strutting and challenging *your* right to drive on *its* roadway; a black bear sow and her cubs, perched on a cut slope, watching passing cars with interest. After 75 years, the Skyline Drive has blended with nature and has become a part of the ecosystem of Shenandoah National Park. This roadway was created from avarice, dreams, and the sweat and tears of countless unemployed men and boys. Along this long and winding road, history and nature meld. Drive slowly and enjoy the view.

Photograph/Illustration Credits

Most of the photographs in this publication are from the Shenandoah National Park museum collections. Several, however, have come from the American Memory collections of the Library of Congress (LOC). Photograph 3 was taken by Jack Delano, May 1941, and is part of the Library of Congress *Chicago Daily News* negative collection (DN-0070595). The photograph on the Part One introductory page was taken by Russell Lee and is part of the FSA-OWI collection at the Library of Congress (LC USF34-035388-D). Illustration 2 came from the Library of Congress American Memory collection and is from the Digital Scriptorium and the John W. Hartman Center for Sales, Advertising & Marketing History, Duke University, Durham, North Carolina.

Neal Lewis, SNP Media Specialist, designed the frontispiece map of the Skyline Drive. Dan Hurlbert, SNP GIS/GPS Specialist, designed Illustration 7, the map of the three park boundaries. Illustrations 15 and 21 (A-D) by author.

Endnotes

1   *Final Report of the Southern Appalachian National Park Commission to the Secretary of the Interior, June 30, 1931,* Washington, D.C., 1931, p. 8.

2   Quoted in "Thomas Jefferson and Sally Hemings," by Jeanette K. B. Daniels, Mariette Glauser, Diana Harvey, and Carol Hubbell Quellette in *Heritage Quest Magazine,* May/June, 2003, <*www.heritagequestmagazine.com*>.

3   These figures are derived from Howard Robert West, "The Horse In America", (1965), in *American Journeys: An Anthology Of Travel In The United States,* E. D. Bennett, ed., Convent Station, New Jersey, 1975, p. 19.

4   Data derived from Daniel B. Klein, and John Majewski, "Turnpike and Toll Roads in Nineteenth Century America," EH.net Encyclopedia, <*www.eh.net/encyclopedia*>, p.3.

5   *Ibid.,* p. 9.

6   Cited in <*http://xroads.virginia.edu*>.

7   "Yellowstone and the Railroads" in "The Yellowstone Net Newspaper," Vol. 1, No 10, Bruce T. Gourley ed., <*http://www.yellowstone.net/newspaper/news103197.htm*>, pp. 1-3.

8   Data from the *Historical Statistics of the United States,* United States Department of Commerce, Bureau of the Census, Washington, 1960, Series Q.

9   Extracted from *ibid.,* p. 459.

10   This quotation and other background materials derived from <*www.fhwa.dot.gov/infrastructure*>. The Federal Highway Administration has posted extensive material on road history. Articles by Richard F. Weingroff and Joyce N. Ritter are of particular interest.

11   *Ibid.,* Article by Richard F. Weingroff.

12   In 1919 Lt. Col. Dwight David Eisenhower was an observer of the United States Army's first transcontinental convoy of military vehicles from Washington, D.C., to San Francisco, California. The trip took two months, primarily because of poor roads. Eisenhower would later remember the trip and signed into law the 1956 Federal Aid Highway Act, which created over 45,000 miles of new interstate highways, the largest construction project ever undertaken in peacetime.

13   The National Park Service Organic Act., 16 U.S.C. 1.

14   There are so many designations for the different types of units in the National Park Service that most NPS employees need a crib sheet to keep the types straight. Traditionally national parks were units that had no encumbrances (that is, outstanding mining or lumber leases), while national monuments were typically smaller units of no lesser cultural or natural value, but ones that might have had existing claims. National monuments were first authorized by the Antiquities Act of 1906 and are created by Presidential Order; national parks can be created only by an Act of Congress.

15   United States Bureau of the Census, *Historical Statistics of the United States.*

16   Chart based on Russ Olsen, *The Organizational Structure of the National Park Service–1917-1985:Administrative History,* Washington, D.C., 1985.

17   Conversion to modern Consumer Price Index equivalents based on web site by John J. McCusker, <*http://eh.net/hmit/ppowerusd*>.

18   McClelland, Linda Flint, *Presenting Nature: The Historic Landscape Design of the National Park Service, 1916-1942,* Washington, D.C., 1993, p. 73.

19 It was not until the 1930s that the government defined the profession of landscape architect as such. Prior to that time professionals with degrees in landscape architecture were defined as landscape engineers.

20 McClelland, *ibid.*, p. 73.

21 *Ibid.*, p. 81.

22 *Ibid.*, p. 108.

23 *Final Report of the Southern Appalachian National Park Commission to the Secretary of the Interior, June 30, 1931,* Washington, 1931, p. 6 ff.

24 *Ibid.*, p. 6.

25 Zerkel's requests for concession contracts and/or for some position where "he could make himself of service" were frequent over the years and, at times, in lengthy epistles. They may be found in NA, NP, Box #444, Entry #7 and in Shenandoah National Park Archives Zerkel Collection (hereinafter SNPZC). The Cammerer to Albright memorandum is in the National Archives files and dated February 7, 1931, shortly before Zerkel received his appointment to work for the Bureau of Public Roads.

26 *Final Report...,* p. 22.

27 The spelling of Jarmans is typical of much early confusion of names within the park. It was not until 1937 that the United States Commission on Nomenclature standardized names in Shenandoah National Park. In this work the historical spelling will be used in quotations, the modern in the balance of the text.

28 *Final Report...,* p. 24. .

29 *Ibid.*, p. 25.

30 *Ibid.*, p. 27.

31 This biographical material was originally researched by the author and is included in the Carson entry in the "C" volume of the *Dictionary of Virginia Biography,* Richmond, Virginia, 2005.

32 *Final Report...,* p. 30 .

33 Quoted in Darwin Lambert, *Shenandoah National Park Administrative History, 1924-1976,* Luray, Virginia, 1979, p. 82.

34 *Ibid.*, p. 87.

35 Hoover, Herbert, "State of the Union Address," December 2, 1930, p. 8, as on <*www.ThisNation.com*>.

36 *Ibid.*, p. 3.

37 Albright to Richey, October 30, 1930, National Archives (College Park), Central Classified Files 1907-1932, National Parks, Shenandoah, 630, Box 444, Entry 7 (hereinafter NA, NP).

38 Zerkel to Carson, December 5, 1930, *ibid.*

39 Albright to Glass, December 11, 1930, *ibid.*

40 Carson to Cramton, *ibid.*

41 Carson to Cramton, January 4, 1931, *ibid.*

42 Letter from Zerkel to Carson, January 26, 1930, SNPZC, Box # 7, Folder #6 and newspaper clippings in NA, NP, 630, Box #444, Entry 7.

43 Carson to Albright, January 31, 1931, NA, Record Group 79, Records of the National Park Service, Records of Key Officials, Records of Horace M. Albright, 1927-1933, Box #7, Entry 17.

44 SNPZC, Box #7, Folder # 7.

45 *Ibid.*

46 NA, NPS, Box #444.

47 SNPZC, Box #7, Folder 7.

48 Zerkel to Cammerer, February 14, 1931, *ibid.*

49 Zerkel to Carson, February 19, 1931, *ibid.*

50 SNPZC, Box #7, Folder 8.

51 Zerkel to Bishop, March 2, 1931, ibid.

52 Albright to Demaray and Vint [Chief Architect], March 18, 1931, NA, NPS, Box #444.

53 Vint to Albright, March 16, 1931, NA., NPS, Box # 445.

54 Although the NPS agreed to drop the public road from Criglersville, it was quietly decided that a private spur road from Rapidan Camp to the Skyline Drive would be built for administrative purposes. Carson purchased the rights-of-way for this side road at the same time as the ones for the Drive.

55 SNPZC, Box #7, Folder 8.

56 Zerkel to Cammerer, February 14, 1931, SNPZC, Box #7, Folder 7.

57 *Ibid.*

58 The shelter was removed in the mid-1930s because the park believed the pit privies for the shelter were contaminating the spring that served as the water source for the adjacent Civilian Conservation Corps camp and the Pinnacles Picnic Grounds fountains.

59 SNPZC, Box #8, Folders 4-5.

60 SNPZC, Box #8, Folder 7.

61 NA, NPS, Box #444. The legislation required that funds be expended within six months, although in the case of the Drive that stipulation would be satisfied by contracts for construction being awarded by July 31, 1931.

62 Deed of H. A. and S.V. Keyser, Page County Deed Book # 96, p. 305.

63 Deed of Sarah A. Brubaker, Page County Deed Book #96, p. 303.

64 Deed of P.P. Long, et. al., to State Commission on Conservation and Development, Page County Deed Book #96, May 23, 1931, and following deeds.

65 A good example of this is the case of H. A. and S. V. Keyser who owned 160 acres in Page County along the route of the Drive. On May 29, 1931 they sold a 100' strip approximately 3,900' long and a 50' wide strip 950' long and the 20 acres east of the strip for $953. Their ultimate condemnation award was $956 meaning that they received $3.00 for the approximately 130 acres remaining of their holdings.

66 Zerkel wrote to Cammerer on July 9, 1931, that "recognizing the handicap [Federal hiring rules] shared by Messrs. Albright and Bishop in doing what the former figured some months ago would be helpful to me and helpful to the N.P.S. and the B.P.R. upon the Skyline Drive project in temporary appointment for me; I have continued my occasional service on Right-of-way work for the State C&D Comm . . . . ," SNPZC, Box #7, Folder 5.

67 Zerkel's billings into the State Commission (copies in SNPZC, Box #7, Folder 6) indicate that he was being paid $8.00/day plus expenses for his services.

68 Demaray to Carson, June 26, 1931, NA, NPS, Box # 445.

69 SNPZC, Box #7, Folder 5.

70 SNPZC, Box #8, Folder 19.

71 SNPZC, Box #7, Folder 5.

72 NA, NPS, Box # 445.

73 Bishop to Demaray, May 23, 1932, *ibid.*

74 Bishop to Carson, May 23, 1932, *ibid.*

75 Carson wrote to Demaray on August 29, 1932 (NA, NPS, Box # 444) and in a rather testy letter stated that "I have your letter of the twenty-fifth, and note that you say at the close as follows: 'Please don't make it embarrassing for me by referring requests [for permits] we can't accede to. Would you please tell me what a public official is for if not for the purpose of 'passing the buck'?" Tempers were clearly near the surface at the State Commission and Washington over the opening of the Drive.

76 SNPZC, Box #7, Folder 8.

77 Demaray to Zerkel, November 17, 1932, SNPZC, Box #8, Folder 7.

78 Letter quoted in Harrisonburg *News-Record*, November 18, 1932, clipping in SNPZC, Box #8, Folder 20.

79 Both letters are in NA, NPS, Box # 444.

80 Byrd to Zerkel, August 17, 1933, SNPZC, Box # 27, Folder 7.

81 *Richmond Times-Dispatch*, August 5, 1934 in <www.vahistory.org/080634.html>.

82 Taylor to Lassiter, July 28, 1934, Shenandoah National Park Resource Management Records (hereinafter SNPRMR), Box # 16, Folder 12.

83 Zerkel to Carson, November 6, 1932, SNPZC, Box #7, Folder 7. Zerkel had written to Carson on the previous July 5th: "The news that you propose to request the survey work for the remainder of the Skyline Highway . . . be done now is certainly good news." (SNPZC, Box # 8, Folder 7).

84 Kelsey was the owner of Highlands Nursery, first in Highlands and later in Linville, North Carolina. He specialized in native ornamental trees and shrubs of the Appalachian Mountains and introduced into cultivation two species of *Rhododendron* and one of *Robinia* (locust).

85 Kelsey to Albright, January 20, 1932, NA, NPS, Box #445, in reference to the December 21 memorandum from Bishop to Demaray.

86 MacKaye to Cammerer, June 13, 1932, *ibid.*

87 Quoted in Darwin Lambert, *op. cit.*, p. 165.

88 Zerkel to Kelsey, November 3, 1932, SNPZC, Box # 7, Folder 8.

89 Albright to Peterson, November 5, 1932, NA, NPS, Box # 445.

90 Kelsey to Albright, November 22, 1932, NA, NPS, Box # 444.

91 Cammerer to Albright, November 5, NA, NPS, Box # 445.

92 *The Columbia Encyclopedia*, Sixth Edition, 2005.

93 *Journal of the American Institute of Architects.*

94 NA, NPS, Box # 455.

95 *Ibid.*

96 Letters from officials in NA, NPS, Box # 481.

97 NA, NPS, Box # 506.

98 MacDonald to Albright, April 12, 1931, *ibid.*

99 Carson to Perkins, May 3, 1933, *ibid.*

100 SNPRMR, File Code 903.

101 Data for northern extension contracts from "Final Construction Reports" for projects SNP 2-A-1 through 2-C-1, SNP Archives.

102 SNPRMR, Box # 16, Folder 11.

103 *Ibid.* and NA, NPS, Box # 506.

104 *Ibid.*

105 *Ibid.*

106 *Ibid.*

107 Demaray to Cammerer (n.d.), *ibid.*

108 *Ibid.*

109 BPR District Engineer Spelman to Demaray, *ibid.*

110 Demaray to MacDonald, February 6, 1936, *ibid.*

111 NA, NPS, Box # 444.

112 Scott to Cammerer, January 27, 1928, *ibid.*

113 Additional information of this topic may be seen at <http://www.nps.gov/shen> in the article "Skyline Drive: A Road to Nowhere."

114 Abbott to Vint, November 30, 1936, SNPRMR, Box # 7, Folder 12.

115 Vint to Abbott, April 10, 1937, SNPRMR, Box # 71, Folder 11.

116 SNPRMR, Box # 71, Folder 10. On June 30, 1961, Public Law 87-71 officially transferred this section of the Blue Ridge Parkway to Shenandoah National Park as opposed to the eight miles being administered by SNP.

117 Quoted in Lambert, *Administrative History*, p. 97.

118 The draft typescript has this as "national areas", but I believe this was a typographic error in the draft.

119 In a speech given to the Virginia Highway Conference, November 12, 1948, Lexington, Virginia, in NA, NPS, Box # 731.

120 Clarke to Demaray, July 6, 1931, NA, NPS, Box # 455.

121 Peterson to Demaray, July 27, 1931, *ibid.*

122 At that time there were no Office of Personnel Management Standards for professional positions. Vint expected his landscape architects to be equally adept at both building and landscape design.

123 Peterson to author, March 1, 2001.

124 Peterson biographies are available at the web site of the American Institute of Architects and <*www.lib.umd.edu/NTL/peterson.html*>, the site of the National Trust for Historic Preservation Library at the University of Maryland, to which Peterson left his papers.

125 SNPRMR, Box # 17, Folder 2.

126 Peterson to Bishop, June 2, 1933, NA, NPS, Box # 455.

127 *Ibid.*

128 There was no Senior Landscape Architect at SNP in these years. The titles were based on grade ranking, not local position.

129 See <*www.nps.gov/whmi/educate/ortrtg/ortrtg1.htm*> for a discussion of travel on the Oregon Trail and <*http://library.thinkquest.org/3205/Trans.html*> for a general discussion of transportation speed.

130 Technically the physical force commonly called centrifugal force is actually a lack of centripetal force. Centripetal force acts on a body in motion; centrifugal on a body at rest.

131 An excellent discussion on the spiral curve is Mary E. Myers, "Iron and Asphalt: The Evolution of the Spiral Curve in Railroads and Parkways", in "Public Roads" (USDOT, Federal Highways Administration), <*www.tfhrc.gov/pubrds/septoct01/spiral.htm*>.

132 NA, NPS, Box # 455.

133 J. K. Summerville (BPR) to Jr. Landscape Architect Lynn Harriss, December 19, 1934, SNPRMR, Box # 18, Folder 10.

134 Benson to Summerville, December 22, 1934, *ibid.*

135 NA, NPS, Box # 731.

136 McClelland, Linda Flint, *op. cit.,* p. 123.

137 Ernest Davidson (Landscape Architect at Mt. Rainier) to Thomas Vint (Chief Landscape Architect, NPS), Report on ECW Work at Mt. Rainier, Third Enrollment Period, 1934) in McClelland, *op. cit.*

138 "Report to Chief Architect, Sequoia National Park, October 1, 1934 to April 1, 1935," *ibid.*, p. 213.

139 Peterson to Bishop, April 29, 1931, NA, NPS, Box # 455.

140 NA, RG 79, 330, 14, 23, 1-3.

141 Quoted in Lambert, *op. cit.,* p. 113.

142 *Ibid.*

143 NA, NPS, Box # 455.

144 *Ibid.*

145 Harriss to Peterson, July 12, 1934, SNPRMR, Box # 16, Folder 12.

146 SNPRMR. Box # 16, Folder 11.

147 *Ibid.* Many automobiles in use at the time Marys Rock Tunnel was constructed still did not have electric headlights or did not have interior switches for the lights. The first modern sealed beam headlight was invented in 1924 and the floor switch for headlights came into being in 1927. Sealed beam headlights were not legally required until the 1940s. Marys Rock Tunnel was constructed, and the lighting discussion occurred, in the transition period in which all new cars came equipped with electric headlights. Thus lighting the tunnel ultimately became unnecessary, although recently uncovered photographic evidence indicates lights were installed in 1932 but probably damaged by ice the first winter.

148 Demaray to Peterson, NA, NPS, Box # 444.

149 SNPRMR, Box # 18, Folder 11.

150 *Ibid.*

151 Rogers to Peterson, August 14, 1934, SNPRMR, Box # 18, Folder 11.

152 Harriss to Rogers, June 20, 1934, SNPRMR, Box # 16, Folder 12.

153 SNPRMR, Box # 18, Folder 11.

154 Drawings from SNPRMR, Box # 16, Folder 9.

155 NA, NPS, Box # 455.

156 Austin to Demaray, July 2, 1931, *ibid.*

157 Horace M. Albright notation on copies of correspondence related to the guardrail disputes included in Demaray to Peterson, July 13, 1931, *ibid.*

158 Demaray to Peterson, July 30, 1931, *ibid.*

159 MacDonald to Albright, October 12, 1932, *ibid.*

160 Oral history interview with Horace M. Albright made April 14, 1969 by R. Taylor Hoskins, E. Ray Schaffner, and Bruce McHenry, SNPRMR, Oral History Collection, Box # 1.

161 Drawing from "Plans, Bid, Bid Bond, Special Provisions, and Supplemental Specifications, Project 3D3…," SNPRMR, Box # 2, Folder 8.

162 Harriss's memoranda are in SNPRMR, Box # 17, Folder 2.

163 *Ibid.*

164 *Ibid.*

165 Peterson to Eugene Stuart, c/o Louisville Automobile Club, August 14, 1935, SNPRMR, Box # 18, Folder 10.

166 Benson to Peterson, August 25, 1935, SNPRMR, Box # 16, Folder 9.

167 September 10, 1935, *ibid.*

168 Associate Highway Engineer (no signature) to Spelman, District Engineer, BPR, February 19, 1941, SNPRMR, Box # 2, Folder 8.

169 SNPRMR, Box # 16, Folder 7.

170 *Ibid.*

171 Over the years the attempts by the Virginia Department of Transportation to shut down the historic spring enclosure on Route 211 between Panorama and Sperryville, used intensively for many decades by devotees of the water quality, have been watched by the author with interest. VDOT continually attempts to remove the spout within the historic masonry enclosure through which the water is conducted. Without fail, after every removal someone reinstalls something that will allow bottles to be filled.

172 Benson to Vint, December 31, 1935, SNPRMR, Box # 18, Folder 11.

173 Arthur Halsted to the Honorable Howard W. Smith, October 26, 1932, NA, NPS, Box # 455.

174 May 18, 1935, SNPRMR, Box # 16, Folder 11.

175 Benson to Peterson, May 24, 1935, *ibid.*

176 Peterson to Lassiter, May 28, 1935, *ibid.*

177 May 29, 1935, *ibid.*

178 April 18, 1938, SNPRMR, Box # 16, Folder 6.

179 Taylor to Vint, April 21, 1938, *ibid.*

180 Benson, Harvey P., "The Skyline Drive: A Brief History of a Mountaintop Motorway," *The Regional Review*, Vol. 4, No. 2, February, 1940, p. 4.

181 Ludgate to Peterson, July 27, 1931, NA, NPS, Box # 455.

182 Ludgate to Peterson, NA, NPS, Box # 422.

183 Peterson to Bishop, June 2, 1933, SNPRMR, Box # 17, Folder 2.

184 SNPRMR, Box # 16, Folder 10.

185 Kelsey to Cammerer, October 28, 1939, Cammerer Personal Papers, NA, NPS.

186 Kelsey to Albright, November 25, 1932, NA, NPS,
Box # 444. This philosophy was possibly responsible
for the introduction of oriental bittersweet to the park.
The highly invasive vine, quite similar in appearance
to the native, still exists and resists control in areas
near the CCC camp nurseries at Big Meadows and
park headquarters in Luray.

187 Photocopy of Knox's report in park Interpretive
Division files.

188 Data compiled by author from Shenandoah National
Park CCC camp monthly reports for periods 13 & 14,
NA, Record Group 79.

189 "Summary of Field Planting, April 1945." Copy at
SNPA. Location of original unknown.

190 Illustration a detail from 19 Sheets of Drawings for
Projects 2a-2b, from NA, NPS, Box # 330.

191 Bert to Rogers, August 20, 1934, SNPRMR,
Box # 16, Folder 12.

192 Ludgate to Peterson, July 27, 1931, NA, NPS,
Box # 455.

193 "General Planning," Tentative Outline, February 1929,
NA, Record Group 79, cited in McClelland, *op. cit.*,
p. 174.

194 Cammerer to Albright, November 30, 1932, NA, NPS,
Cammerer Personal Correspondence, Box # 445.

195 February 25, 1935 quoted in John C. Paige, *The
Civilian Conservation Corps and the National Park Service*,
1933-1942, Washington, D.C., 1985, p. 106.

196 Waugh, *op. cit.*, p. 2.

197 Benson, Harvey P., " The Skyline Drive: A Brief
History of a Mountaintop Motorway," *The Regional
Review*, Vol. 4, No. 2, February, 1940, p. 9, SNPRMR,
Box # 89, Folder 2.

198 Scudder Griffing to G. Y. Carpenter, March 31, 1942,
SNPRMR, Box # 2, Folder 8.

199 Department of the Interior "Annual Reports" (1941,
1946, and 1947), cited in Lambert, *op. cit.*, p. 299.

200 *Ibid.*

201 Regional Director Cox to Superintendent Edwards,
Shenandoah NP, July 31, 1956, SNPRMR, Box # 62,
Folder 3.

202 Department of the Interior "Annual Report" (1955),
op. cit., p. 314.

203 C. J. Wilfong, Highway Engineer Technician to C. E.
Kinney, District Engineer, BPR, September 5, 1963,
SNPRMR, Box # 62, Folder 3.

204 "Park Road Standards (Draft)," March 30, 1984, p. 1,
SNP General Files, Folder for Roads and Trails
1982-1984.

205 *Ibid.*, p. 2.

Index